Site Planning

Kevin Lynch

Site Planning

The M.I.T. Press
Massachusetts Institute of Technology
Cambridge, Massachusetts

Preface

Site planning is the art of arranging buildings and other structures on the land in harmony with each other. This book is intended to be an introduction to the art, an exposition of its principles, and a condensed technical reference. It will be of interest to students and to professional city planners, architects, landscape architects, and civil engineers. But those who enjoy the urban landscape, or who are concerned with the social issues which it generates, may also find some pleasure in it.

There is not much that is original in these pages, except perhaps for the way they are put together. The ideas come from many sources, and have been so condensed, reorganized, and interpreted that they can rarely be referred to a single source. My education in architecture and its roots in the land began with Frank Lloyd Wright, who opened my eyes. Since then, I have been able to work or to teach with skilled men, and to learn thereby: Lawrence Anderson, Robert Woods Kennedy, Ralph Rapson, John Myer. Gyorgy Kepes and his ideas are present as always.

Several expert site planners have made important comments on early drafts of this text: Hideo Sasaki, Julian Whittlesey, Ralph Eberlin. Mark Sagal of the Perini Corporation was helpful in checking my cost figures, and Robert Newman in advising me on exterior acoustics. Rodney Freebairn-Smith took on the demanding task of searching for photographic illustrations. The text has grown gradually out of notes for a course in site planning, beginning with an original nucleus by Draveaux Bender on sewer and water systems. Here and there he will find fragments of his original work.

My best teachers have been the students of architecture and city planning at M.I.T.

Cambridge, Massachusetts   KEVIN LYNCH
March, 1962

Contents

I

Fundamental Technique

Chapter 1

The Art of Site Planning

Site planning is the art of arranging an external physical environment in complete detail. Site planners are all those who deal with structures and the land, whose plans can be carried out in one continuous foreseeable process, according to one original design, under the control of one agency, inclusive of all the details of engineering, landscaping, and architecture. Site planners may be concerned with areas as small as a cluster of five or six single-family houses, or even with a single building and its ground, or they may plan something as large as the layout of a complete small town. Site planning is not a separate profession, although it may be practiced as a specialty. It is a design problem that lies on the boundaries between architecture, engineering, city planning, and landscape architecture, and is practiced by professionals of all these groups. At the upper end of the scale, it is to be distinguished from city planning or urban design, where control is incomplete and development is never terminated. At the lower end site planning may be separated from the design of objects such as buildings or bridges, from interior design, and from the layout of small and isolated exterior settings such as gardens.

The site is a crucial aspect of the environment. It has an impact that is biological, social, and psychological. It sets limits to the things that people can do, and makes possible their doing what they otherwise could not. For some

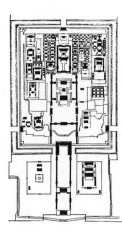

Peking: The Inner City

4

age groups it is the dominant environment for long periods of time. Its influence outlives the individual structure, since the site organization tends to persist for generations.

It was once fashionable to say that the physical environment determined the character of the life that went on in it, and then later in reaction to insist that this environment was of no consequence at all. Each of these views seems to rest primarily on the other's fallacies. Organism and environment are in constant interaction, and each has influences on the other. Environment is both social and physical. One cannot predict the character of a man from the jungle he lives in, but neither can one foretell what he will do or feel without knowing something of the jungle. The man and his habitat must be known together.

Designers of the environment quite naturally tend to overemphasize the importance of the physical shell they are creating, to think that their personal addition will have an overwhelming influence on those who later come to use it. It would be more accurate to describe their new form as only a further modification of the continuous total interplay between inhabitants and their surroundings.

Is it necessary to make site plans? Could not building groups be allowed to grow "naturally," just as many handsome old towns seem to have done? Unfortunately roads, buildings, and even gardens are not plants, they do not grow. They are placed and shaped by someone's decision or plan, however limited and careless that decision may be. The real issue is not whether sites should be planned, but rather how extensive and comprehensive plans should be. Many influences push us toward site organization at a larger scale: the economic advantages of quantity development, the growing complexity and interdependence of site facilities, the tempting possibilities of comprehensively-designed environments, now that we can afford to build them. But regardless of the issue of scale, a site of any size must somehow be organized, if only by piecemeal decision.

A formal design process has become necessary to create this organization, as more building is done with standardized units, in large projects, and at a rapid rate. There is often no chance for consultation with the ultimate consumer, and no time for that gradual adjustment of use and structure to site that guided the site organizations of so much older development.

Thus the professionally prepared site plan is a strategic link in the creation of environment, although it is often

FIGURE 1 *The Royal Crescent at Bath .*

treated as a minor accompaniment to the decisions of engineers, architects, or builders. It is commonly a hurried and
conventional layout, in which details are left to chance and
local custom; or an abstract framework, a "subdivision," to
which buildings and uses are later mechanically attached; or
a last-minute effort to fit a previously designed building to
some piece of available land.

Site planning has acquired new importance, but it is an
old art which has been practiced with skill in other times and
places. One thinks of such magnificent building groups as
the Imperial Palace in Peking, the center of Pergamum, the
Katsura Palace near Kyoto, the crescents of Bath, the Italian
squares of the Renaissance, or many small New England
settlements. Yet site design in this country today is monotonously conventional, careless, shallow, and ugly.

*References 52, 53,
55, 60*

The Nature of Site Planning

Site planning locates structures and activities in three-
dimensional space, and the differences that arise from spatial
arrangement are the meat of the matter: differences in proportion, volume, density, shape, grain, pattern, or linkage.
Small modifications in space pattern have disproportionately
large effects. Other aspects of site planning, however important, follow after this.

FIGURE 2 *The Inca settlement of Machu Picchu, marvelously fitted to its precipitous site high in the Peruvian Andes.*

The final development, in its interaction with its inhabitants, acts as an indivisible whole within which no one element can be changed without having an effect throughout the entire field. It consists, not just of buildings and streets, but of a whole complex of structures, natural forms, climate, texture, and detail, above, below, and at the surface. The complexity and delicacy of these relationships make site planning a time-consuming operation.

While resulting in a complex of forms in space, the plan begins with two things: the human purposes for which the change is being made, and the pre-existing web of things and relationships which is the site itself. Each site, natural or man-made, is unique, and all its parts have meaning in relation to the whole. The essential quality of that whole must be understood, not only because the site will impose certain practical limitations, but also because it will contain new potentialities, and because a plan, however radical, must maintain some continuity with the surroundings in which it is placed. A plan necessarily disturbs a site, but it should enhance and not violate it, whether it practices conservative adaptation or bold rearrangement. Coming to understand a locality requires time and effort. The site planner develops an automatic anxiety about the spirit of place: that total set of existing relations that flows over artificial boundary lines.

Equally important, and often strangely glossed over, are the human ends to be met by a new plan. All too frequently these purposes are implicit but never clearly put and clearly evaluated, and thus in the end they are poorly served. Often they are in conflict among themselves. They must be made articulate before they can be rationally compromised, before the plan can be shaped to meet them or be tested for success. Is it privacy or neighborliness that is being sought, or is it some particular balance between these two? Before he begins the site designer must formulate his objectives in as general a form as he can, without rising to platitudes which are meaningless in physical terms. Later, he must be prepared to test his proposals by those same objectives.

Although a site plan aims at some concrete reorganization which is considered permanent once achieved, that new organization will in fact soon change. New users, new social customs, or a new technology will modify it. The plan must foresee these changes as far as possible, and beyond that be flexible enough to allow adaptation without agony. The site plan is only a new modification in a continuous series of modifications. Every site has a long history, which bears on its present. Every site will have a future, over which the designer will exercise only slight control. He peers anxiously into that future as far as he can, but he realizes that he is operating at a single point in a long succession, and that others will have to adjust his plan to some new demand.

The techniques and principles to be discussed here are based on present technology and present social organization. The technology is sure to change, undermining many trusted standards. Society and human aspirations will change more slowly, but will in the end affect the design more radically. The materials in this text that may be more permanently useful are the processes of analysis or solution, the concepts of organization, space, site, or purpose, and the standards which refer primarily to the biological and psychological nature of men. Other parts of this book will lose their usefulness more rapidly. The designer must always begin by assuming that he is ignorant of the site and the group for whom he is building, that his previous standards cannot be applied, and that whatever he does will soon undergo the first of a series of continuous modifications.

Site planning, then, is the organization of the external physical environment up to the largest scale at which it can still be subject to unified and complete control; it deals with structures, land, and the entire complex of physical forms above, below, and on the surface; it has at its heart the disposition of objects and activities in three-dimensional space; it begins with the careful analysis of site and purpose; and it concludes with a pattern which interacts as a totality with its users, and which is subject to continuous future development and change. The technical drawings produced — grading plans, utility layouts, structural locations — are simply the conventional means of recording this complex organization.

Part I deals with the fundamentals: the analysis of site and purpose, land use and circulation design, visual form and the modification of climate, and the controls and processes of site planning. It summarizes the basic principles, techniques, and issues. In Part II there are more detailed chapters on landscape materials and earthwork; the engineering of utilities and of streets and ways; observations on particular types of site planning such as housing, shopping centers, industrial estates, and large institutions; and data on comparative costs. These later chapters, in particular, contain information that is likely to go out of date. It bears repetition that technical data, however useful, must always be regarded with suspicion wherever it conflicts with basic objectives or is to be applied to cultures or regions other than our own. Nevertheless, Part II is an essential part of the text as a whole and not a series of afterthoughts. The designer should be familiar with this kind of data, even if it must be modified twenty years from now, or two continents away.

Chapter 2

The Analysis
of Site and Purpose

The existing site, and the purposes for which it will be modified, are the two sources from which the design springs. These two sources are curiously interrelated, in a circular way. Purpose cannot be stated until the limitations that the site will impose are known, and the site itself cannot be analyzed until the purpose for which it will be used is set forth. Previous experience is needed to break into this circle: to set realistic purposes before a particular site has been analyzed, or to judge a site before detailed purposes are known.

Concurrently with the study of site, therefore, the designer is engaged in clarifying his objectives for modifying that site. If these objectives are not stated specifically, he will make his choices on the basis of unconscious assumption. His freedom for maneuver will be limited because of those hidden assumptions, his true objectives may not be served, and unforeseen consequences can develop. Objectives, like site, are always specific and particular, and those chosen will depend on the situation and the values of the designer and his client. If the client is a corporate one, or, even more difficult, an anonymous group, then special techniques of search and evaluation must be used to develop the objectives. Despite this difficulty, something can still be said in regard to the formulation of goals in general.

The direct functional goals are usually easy to state and to test: "to house 100 families," "to allow a flow of 2000 cars per hour." The more general objectives are harder to put. The difficulty lies in the level of generality to use: shall it be "the most comfortable environment possible," or that "all south and west façades are to be shaded by trees?" The first is so general as to be useless in testing a proposal, and the second dictates the solution before design has begun.

It is preferable to put objectives in as concrete a form as possible without fixing a particular physical solution. Thus, in the example given, the objective might have been stated as "to maintain outdoor summer temperature and humidity within the range of comfort," which can be accomplished by many techniques in addition to shading by trees.

Beyond this question of the level of generality, the objectives should be significant ones: their application should discriminate between alternative solutions and cause decisions to be made. Thus "minimum cost" is a test likely to separate one reasonable plan from another, while "all houses to be accessible" may not. The set of objectives should also be complete so that it contains all the important criteria. When the plan meets the stated objectives, the designer should be confident that his major purposes have been fulfilled.

As far as possible, the goals should be consistent with one another, but normally they will conflict to some extent. For example, a client will desire minimum cost and maximum floor space. There must then be some principle of weighting that will tell one how far to go in sacrificing space for cost. This weighting can only be stated approximately at the beginning, and develops as the design develops, as alternatives are chosen and rejected. The objectives are analyzed early, but continue to be refined throughout the design process.

Part of a site designer's professional stock is his accumulated experience on how various objectives can be achieved. He is constantly checking his environment and criticizing site plans which have become reality: does this device in fact encourage social communication? how has the microclimate changed? has the plan adapted easily? We would be in a far better position if we had thorough analyses of the real effects of past work. Too often experiments are made on hunches and then are imitated elsewhere without a study of actual results. Even if we had such analyses, however, the designer would still have to supplement them with personal observation.

It is a common error for a designer to assume his own values in developing a plan, disregarding the values, habits, and objectives of the people who will inhabit the new development. This error is aggravated by the fact that most designers are members of a small social class. They must make a major effort to break out of their own value system and to understand the desires and customs of the future site users. Even if a planner decides not to accept these desires and customs, and wishes to modify them in some way, he must first understand the existing situation from which he hopes to depart.

Typical Goals

While the goals of any plan are never standard, there are some general objectives which tend to recur and are worth remembering as criteria against which plan alternatives can be checked:

1. *Functional adequacy:* Will there be enough light? Is there a suitable place to play baseball? Is there room to pile snow? Will the soil support this structure? Direct questions of functional adequacy are the first to be asked and the easiest to answer. They refer to the original motives for making a plan, and can be checked by a mental run through the motions of the various activities that would be carried on within the new environment.

2. *Optimum communication:* Most plans are effective to the degree that goods, persons, and information can circulate easily within their bounds. Some of the means of achieving good communication will be discussed in Chapters 3 and 4. The goal may also include the stimulus or encouragement of communication, or it may be qualified by stating that the purpose is to permit maximum communication as a possibility, while guaranteeing the control of communication by the individual. For example, much design discussion, particularly in regard to housing, revolves about the question of communication between people. How can neighborliness and community solidarity be encouraged? Indeed, do we want neighborliness or do we desire privacy and independence? More social interaction at the local scale may mean less interplay at the larger scale, and vice versa. Too much interaction can have as disastrous an effect as too little. Social, rather than physical, environment probably plays the dominant role here. In the present state of our knowledge, the best goal may be to provide as much oppor-

tunity for neighborly communication as possible, while leaving the choice of sociability or privacy to the individual.

3. *Choice:* Where the individual is highly valued, and where it is difficult to predict the desire of the site users, it is common to set a goal of choice: an environment which maximizes the freedom of the users to choose their own habitat, facility, service, activity, or neighbors. Such an objective is rarely served by laissez-faire, or random order. Normally, the necessary variety, the ease of selection and access, and the degree of individual control required by this goal, are all attainable only by careful planning.

4. *Cost:* The development should be achieved and maintained at the least cost of labor, material resource, or organizational effort. Given the functions to be served and the standards to be met, which plan is cheaper? Should the standards be changed to give a more economical solution? What will be the effect on maintenance costs? What should be the balance between initial cost and maintenance cost? Will the plan call for more community effort and control than the community is willing or able to supply?

It is surprising that these questions, which are usually uppermost in the minds of those who make development decisions, are so often irrationally answered. Last-minute savings may be made by cutting out "luxuries," but there is rarely a critical examination of the relative cost of basic alternatives or a rational analysis of the relative importance of first and continuing costs. Future maintenance problems are sometimes neglected by designers who are oriented to the initial creation of a new entity rather than to the continuing effort needed to maintain its usefulness.

Cost is an allocating device and therefore as a criterion it is in conflict with most other objectives. A balance must be struck between cost and each desired end. As in most other fields, good work is rarely cheap. To minimize cost without knowing the point below which other objectives cannot reasonably be met is a certain way to achieve the waste of resources. It is extravagant to build an inexpensive bridge that will not stand, or a cheap development that will be a continuing eyesore.

The designer is regularly and painfully confronted with this particular dilemma of objectives. He must determine the point at which he will advise against construction in the light of available resources and the importance of the objectives involved. This point may be closer to zero cost in site planning than in other arts because of the range of possibilities and the relative cheapness of materials, but it exists nevertheless. Often the cost differential between good and bad work may lie more in the additional design time required than in the actual construction cost. Although this particular labor cost may be quite small in proportion to total cost and project life, these immediate outlays will often loom irrationally large to the client.

5. *Health and Comfort:* It would seem obvious that any man-made environment should contribute to the health, comfort, and survival of men. Frequently, however, a client may not be concerned with anything more than minimum standards of sanitation or structural safety. The responsibility for the public health then falls on the designer, who must consider such matters as accident prevention, an optimum climate, or low noise levels. Many of the factors involved here are fairly well known, even if often neglected in practice. In contrast, the important relationship of environment to mental health is as yet largely obscure.

6. *Adaptability:* Since sites will always undergo modifications of function, the design should facilitate readaptation. The designer will look into the future as far as he can, and any foreseen changes can be provided for. But such future estimates are limited to short periods and are uncertain. Furthermore, most people need some "give" or plasticity in their environment; they wish to mold it themselves to some extent, to enter into active relation with it. Despite the natural obsession of a client with present need, any plan should be tested for the scope it gives to individual action by its users, and for how gracefully it will accommodate to future change.

At the same time, most people are disturbed by sudden or sweeping change. Therefore it is advisable to preserve some link of continuity between a new development and the previous use of the site, and also to provide a pattern within which future change can occur without destroying the general framework of form.

7. *Image Quality:* If it is to be livable and enjoyable, a development should be shaped to present a vivid and coherent visual image. Moreover, it should seem meaningful, continuous with its surroundings, expressive of its functions and of the aspirations of its builders. These esthetic criteria will be discussed again.

See Chapter 5

These general goals are not settled for all time. Even where they apply, they will have to be reinterpreted, weighted, and made precise in each case. In one plan, cost will be the overwhelming consideration; in another, it will be preservation of a link with the past or provision for future growth. But the factors listed are common enough to be useful as a check list in judging the value of plans and as a start in drawing up a set of objectives prior to developing a plan. Their very obviousness often causes them to be neglected and overridden in the usual site planning process.

Site Analysis

The analysis of a site depends on the use to which it is to be put. The same piece of ground will be seen quite differently by a quarryman, a fortifications engineer, or a building contractor, and each view will be correct for the given purpose. There are site factors which by experience seem to be influential in most building development, but an unusual purpose may invalidate them. No site can be studied pedantically, hoping that by describing all the factors in some standardized list the essential nature of a locality will be discovered. The purpose of the reconnaissance must be uppermost in mind and determines what is being looked for, even if that purpose is simply to find out the use to which the site can best be put.

In the past, an understanding of site was often more advanced than it is today. Since earlier people had less power to change the site, they were perforce more keenly aware of the limitations it presented. Magical beliefs had an even greater influence. If a locality was the home of a local spirit, one avoided disturbing that home without due precaution. These precautions included ritual acts and the anxious study of local configuration, and entailed the careful adjustment of human structures to that configuration. The development was in consequence closely knit to the site. In most cultures land is sacred, a thing not to be violated by any upstart human agency. It is enduring, powerful, extensive; the home of spirits and the dead; the productive mother upon whom human life depends.

As we discarded these religious ideas, and as we increased our power to impose site changes, we have tended to lose the useful by-product of those ancient attitudes: we no longer unconsciously produce developments which work in harmony with their setting, nor erect structures expressive of locality.

Although the completely harmonious and mature site is unusual (and had best be left alone), the completely chaotic and meaningless one is almost nonexistent. Every site, however disturbed, has had some time to experience the mutual adjustment of its elements. Surface flow has created a drainage pattern, plant and animal life has achieved an ecological balance, neighboring structures lean against each other, shops have arranged themselves in relation to the resident population, climate has weathered all alike. Any site is composed of many factors — above, below, and at the ground — but all these factors are interrelated, and have achieved some sort of balance, whether it be static or one that is moving toward another equilibrium.

Because of the complexity of parts and their intricate patterning together, we find that each site is in some measure unique. While it may fit into some general classification, it will have a flavor, an essence, of its own. The words *site* and *locality* should convey the same sense that the word *person* does: a complexity so closely knit as to have a distinct character, a complexity worthy of interest and even of affection.

FIGURE 3   *A fine rural landscape has an obvious harmony and character.*

FIGURE 4 *But the character and harmony of an urban landscape must also be understood.*

These interrelations, this essential character, must be understood by the site designer. Such an understanding will make clear the practical limits imposed upon him, as well as the damage that he may inflict by careless interference. More important, they will reveal to him the hidden potentialities of the place, the points where his design can clarify, build new connections, or develop deeper meanings. The analysis of site is not only a technique for conservatives: it is also an essential prelude to successful revolution.

Subsurface Conditions

To begin with, it is useful to canvass the site factors which are typically most significant in the design of building groups. These include the subsurface factors, the topography, the cover, the climate, and the pattern of existing land use.

Subsurface conditions refer in particular to the foundation material and to the level of the water table. The rock and earth below ground have practical importance primarily for the way in which they can be excavated, their characteristics of drainage, and the manner in which they will support structural foundations. They are also significant for the way in which they have set the stage for all the visible detail of the site.

The characteristics of soils in place depend on soil type, internal structure, and moisture content. Critical foundation problems must be studied by soil engineers, using laboratory methods of analysis, but a surprisingly good general picture of the difficulties to be encountered in ordinary development, composed of local roads and low buildings, can be gained from field reconnaissance. Other sources of information include small test pits, agricultural and geological maps, existing cuttings and foundations, and the experience of previous builders and engineers. Natural soil components may be divided into six basic groups; these classifications and their significance are described in Chapter 13.

Page 212

Lying over the subsoil, which will act as the foundation material, is a relatively thin layer of organic topsoil. This is the essential medium for the growth of plants, and centuries are required to build it up. It is of prime value not only for any particular development, but as a part of the general human heritage. It must be conserved.

At some greater depth is the water table: the line below which the interstices between the soil grains are full of water. Where the table is too low, supplying water may be expensive or impossible. Where the table is less than six or eight feet below the surface, all development costs are increased: excavations must be sheeted and pumped out; utilities and basements must be waterproofed; some soils may be untrustworthy as foundation material. In particular, one avoids building over a subsurface water course or filling in surface drainage courses without adequate provision for the resulting underground flow.

Therefore certain subsurface conditions are danger signals calling for more detailed and expert attention: rock lying close to the surface; a high water table or an underground stream; the appearance of soft clay, loose silt, or fine water-bearing sand; any evidence of slides or subsidence; an area that has been a dump or is newly filled; the presence of swamps, peat, or muck in more than small isolated pockets.

Surface Characteristics

The topographic surface, the boundary between earth and air, has particular implications for site development.

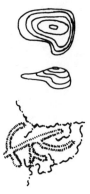

Sometimes it determines the organization of the plan. The gradient of paths, the flow of utilities, the use of areas, the disposition of buildings, the visual aspect, are all affected by it. The designer must grasp the characteristic of the land form as a whole and identify its key points for the purpose he has in mind. He must have a sense of its scale, of the meaning of various slopes, and of the relation of its plan shape to its perspective shape. In most cases the existing topography already·has an underlying order brought about by the flow of surface water. Thus the basic modelling of the ground can often be analyzed by the construction of ridge and drainage lines.

Slopes may be classified according to the use for which they are suitable: the flat ground, usable for intensive activity; the easy grades, suitable for movement and informal activity; and the steep land, difficult to use or to move over. Thus the topography can be analyzed piecemeal, outlining the areas suitable for intensive use, the badly drained portions, and so on. Regions where the surface is difficult and tends to determine the layout of circulation may be distinguished from gentler regions where the paths can be disposed in many different patterns. There may be "passes," restricted localities which offer the only opportunity to cross some rough terrain, or there may be lines along which an approach would develop a very special visual sequence. There may be points which have commanding views, areas which are distinct visual units, or localities which are best oriented to the sun. At times some of these characteristics may become dominant and practically inalterable. A design may have to take for granted the necessity of developing a particular view, avoiding certain ground, or preserving a special tree.

Some aspects of visual analysis of topography are similar to military reconnaissance for fields of fire, which are like lines of sight. Concepts like defile or military crest are useful. For example, the military crest, or brow of a hill, which is the point below the true crest where the grade changes so that the downward slope is open to view, is often a more strategic point at which to place a structure than at the very top. Conversely, the true crest may be the best location for activities which are meant to be visually isolated from the valley bottoms.

In addition to this analysis by parts, the total pattern of a piece of ground must also be discovered. This·will usually become clear only after detailed analysis and much trial of alternative plans. At this point one can say that for the particular purpose in mind the essential character of the site is a certain simple configuration of area, line, and key point, a certain basic set of landscape forms, the rest being mere detail or accident. The design is based on this knowledge. There are landscape families, which have a common pattern and typical associations of detail: the bushy pasture of New England, the American ribbon shopping street, the coastal mangrove swamp, or the intricate farming pattern of Tuscany. But each particular site must also be studied on its own.

References 6, 39

The existing topography is an equilibrium of surface and drainage, and the use and cover is normally also in balance with it. In the scale of geological time all surfaces are changing, but in the scale of a human generation these natural shifts are often very slow. Wherever the ground is disturbed by man, or even where the intensity of use changes, the plant cover and surface form must usually be modified in its turn. Only particularly fine plant specimens, or relatively large areas of ground without structures, can be preserved.

Climate and Acoustics

Each site has a general climate, which it shares with the surrounding region, and a microclimate, a modification of the general climate, which may be peculiar to a very small area. The general climate is expressed in a set of average data for the region, covering such phenomena as solar angle, days of sunlight, ranges of temperature and humidity, precipitation, and wind direction and force. This information, broken down by major seasons of the year, has a basic influence on the entire plan: the orientation of structures and their shielding or exposure to sun, the equipment for cooling or heating, the fenestration, the materials, the cover and planting in general. In addition, the typical light condition will profoundly affect the visual form.

Regional climates are discussed on page 219

If human beings are to be comfortable, there are certain optimum ranges of daylight, of air movement and purity, and of temperature and humidity. The plan modifies the existing climate to approximate this optimum condition. The means for making this approximation will vary with each climate, and it is only too common to bring forms suitable for one climate into another completely different one: to plant lawns in the desert, put colonial houses in the tropics, or use stuccoed half-timber in the New England wilderness.

Beyond these general climatic factors, there are surprising variations in the microclimate of a site due to cover or topography. Wind speed and temperature will vary markedly within a few feet of elevation or from spot to spot. The site planner takes great interest in these effects since they are not recorded in official data and since he can take advantage of them in adapting his site. The orientation and form of the topography, the type of surface materials, the plant cover and the location of structures, the presence or absence of water, all have striking impact on the micro-*See Chapter 6* climate, on the quality of light, and the propagation of noise. If he is familiar with these effects, the designer can learn much about the local climate by a careful look at the site, by talks with local people, by the way in which older structures have weathered, and particularly by the type, condition, and budding time of existing plants.

Man-Made Characteristics

Finally, there are many man-made characteristics to be studied in analyzing a site. The essential elements almost always include the accessibility to external facilities or persons — schools or pupils, shops or customers, workplaces or labor force, supplies or outlets — plus the relation of the site to the general circulation system — the highways, footpaths, railroads, transit lines, and airports. It will always be important to know how the land is used within the site and around its borders, the type of activity and the type and condition of structures. Quite often the social and economic status of these uses, or their visual form, will be crucial. It well repays the designer to observe in detail how an area is actually used by its inhabitants. Watching the pattern of truck movement or of the walk to work, spotting the teen-age hangout or the sled run, will be more informative than pages of statistics. The location, elevation, and capacity of any technical facilities in or near the site must also be mapped: roads, power or water supply, disposal systems, or communications lines. The more accessible, urbanized, and developed a site becomes, the more these man-made features of use, structure, circulation, and utilities become predominant over the factors of soil, topography, and cover.

There are also intangible features which adhere to a site and must be reckoned with. Normally there will be public regulations which affect it in the form of zoning or subdivision regulations, building codes, and official maps. There may be rights which others hold in the area: rights-of-way, easements of various kinds, liens, restrictions due to private covenants, mineral rights, and so on. There are also the less precise but equally significant meanings that people have attached to a site: its history, its sacredness, or the fact that it is the common focus of a larger area.

All of these factors — the conditions below ground, the surface form, activity, and life, the structures and facilities, the bath of air which envelops them, the meanings, rights and regulations — make up the nature of a site. This is always a complex and often a confusing picture. The designer sifts through this mass of data to find the elements which are decisive for his purpose and then fits these elements into some kind of pattern on which he can base his design. He separates the transitory or disappearing features from the more permanent or emergent ones; he discounts the fine old decaying trees in favor of new growth, or distinguishes the form of a hill from the scars of recent excavation. Yet he must not be so strongly directed toward his purpose and so intent on finding a coherent pattern that he misses the facts that might begin to change his purpose, or the facts that do not fit the pattern.

The Process of Site Analysis

Therefore it is often advisable to study a site in two different ways. First, one may search rather aimlessly, forgetting the use to which the area is to be put, looking only at the site itself, and watching for interesting features and revealing clues. This type of unsystematic, almost subconscious, reconnaissance is often productive of information or connections that would otherwise be missed. It will at the very least serve for general orientation. It is usually useful at this point to look briefly at the history of the site, its natural evolution, its former use and associations. Much of the flavor and structure of a place as well as its present direction of change is thereby revealed.

Then a more systematic survey can be undertaken, guided by the purpose to be served. Each piece of ground is now to be tested for its suitability for that purpose. Since the data which could be gathered is potentially endless, no information should be sought unless it appears that it will later influence the design in some significant way. Some types of information are almost always required, such as a topographic map, climatic data, or a survey of land use and circulation. Other types likely to be needed have been indicated in the preceding pages.

Most often the survey will include the preparation of a base map showing the legal lines such as boundaries and easements; the location of utilities, roads, paths, buildings, and walls; the local activities and circulations; the presence of swamps, streams, and water bodies; the general vegetative cover including precise locations of large trees; a notation of rock outcrops and other visible geologic features; contours and the spot elevations of key points; compass directions; and the character of the site environs. Copies of this map will be taken into the field for personal annotation, to get a "feel" for the site by analyzing its character, its views, its approaches, its problems, and its possibilities. The locale should be visited many times, so that it is seen under varied circumstances of weather, light, and activity.

Before the survey begins, a complete schedule of the data to be gathered must be made up. Unfortunately, any standard checklist of information can be viewed with suspicion. The data gathered and the form into which it is put depends on the purpose of the development and the resources available to make the survey. An adequate reconnaissance may consist of a rapid freehand sketch made on the site, or it may require an elaborate technical organization. In either case, it should be as spare and succinct as possible, and must always include personal observation, perhaps partly by car or helicopter, but always in large degree on foot.

Once the information is assembled, it can be put in concise and usable form. It will then be brought to a final point: a graphic and written statement, describing the essential nature of the site for the purpose in hand. The principal problems raised by the location are set down, as well as its basic potentialities and values.

This is the basis on which the design is developed. It will be found that the concept of the site will change as the design unfolds, and that further information almost always comes to light or must be sought for. Site analysis is not a self-contained step which is completed before design begins. First thoughts on design accompany and guide the original reconnaissance, and analysis continues as long as the design is being created.

The image of the site guides the design. It does not dictate the design, nor is there any unique best solution mystically latent in the site waiting to be uncovered. The plan

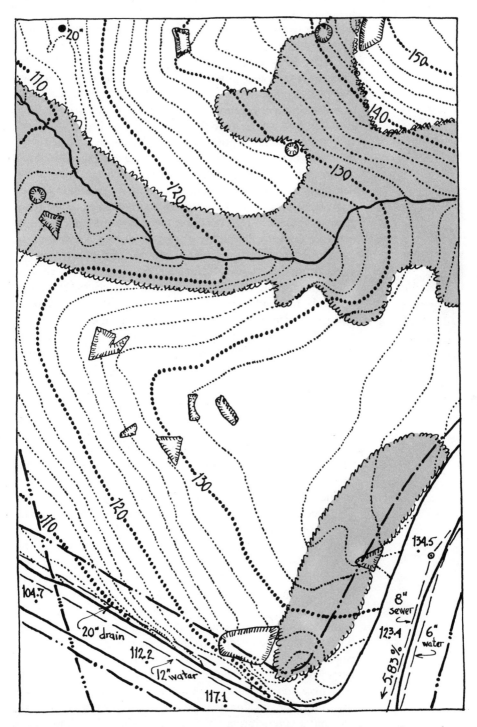

FIGURE 5 *A typical site survey, showing contours, rocks, streams, and vegetation; roads, utilities, and property lines (from a survey by Rowland H. Barnes and Co.).*

develops from the creative effort of the designer himself. But it must respond to the site and not disregard it. Often the designer will be working with the grain of the locality, treating it delicately, only emphasizing its highlights or teasing out its potentialities. Sometimes he will dramatically cut across or deny its nature. This, too, must be knowingly done and can succeed only if the site is thoroughly understood.

It sometimes happens, and should happen more often, that the site is not fixed or chosen before the designer is brought in. In this case, having been given the general objectives, he is involved in the process of site selection, which may be a narrow weighing of two alternatives, or a broad, area-wide search. Site selection uses the same techniques as any site analysis, but a broad search will most often begin by the reduction of possibilities to a handful of alternatives. This is usually done by screening: blocking off on an area map the regions that, in the light of objectives, are unacceptable for such reasons as excessive grade or cost, poor soil, small size, previous development, or lack of access.

The remaining lands not blocked off are then reconnoitred to reject any other obviously unacceptable ones, and the surviving plots are treated as alternative sites, each of which is analyzed in some depth for the most critical factors. These analyses are arranged comparatively, and preliminary layouts are made on each site, since nothing so well illustrates the character of a ground as its influence on the layout itself. From these comparative displays an informed choice can be made. Wherever a real choice exists, this method is preferable by far to the normal process of calling in the planner only after site selection has been made.

Occasionally the designer may be called upon to make just the opposite analysis: given a site, what is its best use? This is a more vague and difficult study. It involves the establishment of a broad social framework of objectives, and within that an array of possible alternate sets of objectives which might govern the use of the land. The site is reconnoitred very thoroughly, particularly in the unsystematic manner, looking for clues and hints in the ground itself. The old Chinese garden designers sat quietly for days in a single place, meditating on its character before they even began to consider its possibilities. In the same way, meditation may suggest new purposes to which ground may be put. Then the possible uses are narrowed to those most feasible, and a comparative set of analyses, including sketch layouts, is made for each set of purposes. On this, and on judgments external to the site such as market or broad social purpose, the choice can be made.

Program

The designer will be involved, to a greater or lesser extent, in the preparation of the detailed objectives, or program, of the plan. This program, which springs from the primary objectives and is influenced by site character, states the quantity, the budgeted cost, and to some extent the quality, of the physical facilities to be provided in the new development.

All too often, the program is considered to be the first step in a plan, being a schedule which is later "fitted" into the site, and of which the design is merely a three-dimensional elaboration. The program should not be primary in this sense. Behind it lie the original objectives, although this is often neglected as a conscious step. The program is limited by available resources and by the site, unless the site is chosen later to fit the program. The program must in addition be influenced by the potentialities of design.

Therefore the designer should be a party to the preparation of the program, and this program should be involved in the constant process of change and refinement as site and design potentialities are uncovered. Not even a sketch program can be prepared before basic objectives are clarified, and before there is some idea of ability to pay, and of the limitations imposed by site or by construction and design technique.

The fully developed program will include a schedule, not only of what facilities are required, but by what time they are to be provided. It may go on to state the chronological order in which the parts should be completed, or their priority order for achieving the client's objectives. In complex developments, the program may be broken down into stages, each of which is a relatively self-sufficient working whole, so that its completion may be separated from succeeding stages by substantial gaps of time.

Chapter 3

The Location of Activities

Once site and purpose have been analyzed, site planning begins with a land use diagram. The site plan locates two things: physical objects and human activities. Land use refers to activity locations, but it also implies the general physical forms that permit those activities, such as an open piece of ground at a recreation location, or a detached house in a low-density residential area. Therefore a land use diagram shows the general functional arrangement of a plan, including types of use, densities, and the links between uses; but only broadly implies the three-dimensional form. The technique may be applied to large areas, employing general categories, or may be used in the organization of a small back yard.

Land use analysis is an abstract technique and has the problem of any abstraction: it often seems bloodless and difficult to bring down to a concrete plan. But it has the power of an abstraction as well: one can consider basic functional relationships with all the accidents of shape stripped away, and decisions can be made on major issues without predetermining detailed form.

The first step in making a land use diagram is to decide on the classes of activity which will be subject to rearrangement. This first step, like most first steps, is treacherously simple. What once is put together in a category is hardly ever divided again: if one uses the classes "industry" and "residence," it will rarely occur to one that some kinds of industry may have different requirements of location, or that living and working in the same building might be a good solution. Therefore the classes of use in any problem must be set with care and divided as finely as will not make their organization too complex. What one looks for are the packages of activity which will not function well unless they are located in one place or which demand similar site characteristics, and not the group of activities that are conventionally put together, or are legally wedded in the zoning ordinance, or seem superficially alike. Thus in a residential area it may simplify the problem to group together the storage of rubbish and the delivery of fuel, but it does not necessarily follow that food delivery or laundry drying should also occur at the same point.

Use classifications in housing, and their linkages, are discussed in Chapter 9

Linkages

When the use classes have been set, then the linkages between them must be analyzed. The links may be movements of people, goods, and wastes, or the communication of information, or they may be connections of amenity, such as the view afforded by a park. The linkages may even be negative, repulsions due to nuisance effects.

Not only the existing links but also the connections that the designer wants to bring about must be analyzed. These may be quite different. For example, there might at present in some area be no contacts between Negro and white, or between faculty members of different departments, or between shopping and parks, but the designer may wish to establish them. He will also give quite a different weight to linkages which will persist despite separation in space, such as the delivery of addressed mail, versus those which are sensitive to spatial location, such as spontaneous communications between people. Furthermore, thought must be given as to how these links may change in the future.

It is not even simply a question of how best to link together a given set of activities. The planner also considers whether additional activities should be brought into the system. Thus in housing developments we find that much of their livability consists in the nonresidential facilities that are accessible to the dwellings: the stores, schools, churches, offices, and recreation centers. An early step in land use analysis is the consideration of what activities *should* be linked with the given ones, and how close this access ought

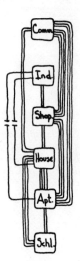

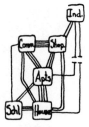

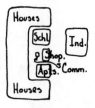

to be. Closeness of access is most accurately measured in terms of time and cost, rather than pure distance. Directness of linkage is the resultant of spatial separation and of the means of communication.

In the diagram in the margin, the components of a small community are connected by lines whose thickness is proportional to the importance of the linkage between them. There are six classes of use. The apartments and houses, and the shops and community facilities, are to be linked as closely as possible. The shops and community facilities should be quite convenient to the apartments, and somewhat less so to the houses; the school should be quite convenient to the houses, somewhat less so to the apartments, with a minor linkage to the community facilities. The factories, finally, should be convenient to the shops, and within reasonable range of the housing, although with some barrier between. The designer is indifferent as to the relation of school and factories. These ideas as to desired linkages are based not only on interactions between activities, but on general ideas as to circulation, visual form, and site character as well.

This diagram might be rearranged to minimize the length and intersection of heavy connections. This rearrangement gives a first clue as to a preferred activity pattern. Both of these are topological diagrams, i.e., they are not to scale and express nothing but the classes of use and their preferred connections.

If the land areas required are drawn roughly to scale, the diagram becomes something that might be applied to the actual site. Each area of the diagram now indicates not only an abstract location, but also a portion of space which is appropriate for the use intended or will be modified to be so. The land use diagram, in other words, implies both activity and the general physical provision for that activity. The space should be of adequate size and appropriate shape, should have the proper climate (guaranteed by enclosure or other means), and should have a floor of suitable slope and texture. These are perhaps the fundamental requirements that influence the choice of location for an activity or dictate the type of structure that should house it.

Modification of climate by siting, structures, and plants is discussed in Chapter 6. Requirements of size and shape are peculiar to each particular use. Some of these requirements for various types of use are touched upon in Chapters 9 and 10. Appropriate ground form also varies, but there is a general scale of slope that is worth remembering since it applies to many uses: slopes under one percent (those rising one foot in one hundred feet) do not drain well, while those under four percent seem flat and are usable for all kinds of intense activity. Slopes between four percent and ten percent appear as easy grades, suitable for informal movement and activity. Slopes over ten percent seem steep, make unfavorable roads, and can be actively used only for hill sports or free play, since gradients above this point require noticeable effort to surmount. A 15 percent slope approaches the limit that an ordinary loaded vehicle can climb for a sustained period. The slope of mowed surfaces must be kept under 25 percent, and slopes over 50 percent or 60 percent cannot be protected from erosion in a humid climate except by cribbing or terracing.

Suitability for use includes suitability for maintenance of that use. Thus park land which is scattered into many irregular fragments, isolated from the road system, will be difficult to keep up and to control. Intricate landscaping may require continuous, expensive care. Even the mere quantity of open space in a plan may be beyond the power of a community to maintain or to protect from encroachment. It is usually preferable to assign open space to some activity which will of itself preserve and maintain it, such as a productive forest or farm, an active park, a golf course, or a cemetery, or, alternatively, to keep it far away from access and potential invasion.

A word of caution is required by anyone who uses land use diagrams: one is liable to oversimplify the total pattern, as well as the basic categories. Pictorial neatness is seductive. Nothing in the land use technique requires that all uses of one type must occur in one location, or that they must not be intermixed with other uses. Distinctions or linkages between use types are often more indeterminate than we imagine. Mixtures of uses may be most desirable for reasons of contrast or continuous use of a site, or to allow for linkages that cannot be foreseen. It may be safer to put the burden of proof on proposals to separate uses in space, rather than on proposals to intertwine them. An arrangement in which use types cluster in a relatively pure state around focal points, but grade outwards into mixtures with other types, is often a natural solution.

Density

Land area requirements involve the concept of density, or the intensity of activity occurring per unit ground area. This density has a far-reaching effect on the site plan and

F.A.R. · 0.75

on the quality of life within it. In the case of residential development it is usually measured in terms of the number of families per unit area, since the family in our culture is a rather stable and independent small unit with many standardized requirements. At a larger scale, densities may be expressed in persons per unit area, or number of employees, or dollars of sales or of value added. Physical density, as opposed to activity density, is most easily expressed in the floor area ratio, or the ratio of gross floor area of a building to ground area. Another commonly used measure is that of rooms per acre.

All measures in use today are thus some variant of an area density. In the future, as population or activity increases, and as technology weakens the connection of structures to ground or makes possible three-dimensional circulation systems, we may turn to measures of cubic density: intensities per unit volume.

The ground area upon which an area density is based may be the immediate building site (giving a net density); the building site plus surrounding streets and other immediately adjacent and necessary open land uses (giving a gross density); or the area of a much larger region, which contains not only the buildings and their immediate circulation but all the necessary services and facilities at a community scale, including local shopping, schools, churches, and playfields (giving a neighborhood density). Many tricks may be played with density standards by shifting from base to base and from definition to definition. For his own protection, the site planner must be aware of these differences and familiar with the concrete results of various abstract numbers.

Reference 26

With lower-density building types, which have land or lots directly assignable to the building, the net density is a fairly precise measure. But when dealing with tall apartments set in open space, it is sometimes difficult to decide where the "immediately adjacent" land stops. Gross density gives a fairer picture of land requirements because it includes streets and nearby open spaces. But it can be vague unless what is to be included is clearly specified. Neighborhood density is a fairly stable measure (as long as local facilities can be separated from nonlocal) and reflects the demand for land which occurs as a result of higher net densities. It is useful for large-scale studies but less so for small site plans.

Despite their difficulties, these quantities must be employed to give scale to a plan. Like other important variables, if they are not used consciously they will appear as thoughtless assumptions. Some sense of the meaning of residential densities in current practice is given in Chapter 9. These types of development and their normal densities are worth committing to memory, although for use as points of beginning rather than as standards.

Usually we find it impossible to say that there is an "ideal" density. Most often, for any given use, there is range of densities outside of which development is likely to be substandard and within which there are a number of breakpoints marking a shift from one character with its particular advantages to another with other advantages. Thus in non-farm housing acceptable net densities may range from one family per acre to 120 families per acre, with lower intensities becoming very costly in terms of services and social equipment, and higher densities substandard in terms of light, air, and open space (given present technology).

Within this total allowable range there are a number of breakpoints defining smaller ranges in which a certain type of structure is most suitable. These breakpoints are also likely to indicate some basic changes in visual or functional character, such as the density below which social isolation is to be expected; or the one above which industrial processes cannot be arranged on a single level. Density also has direct economic effects, so that we can say that in most parts of America today, given land of low cost, the least expensive housing can be provided at net densities of about 15 to 20 families per acre. This depends, of course, not only on land cost, but on technology, standards, and regulations (the fire rules of a generation ago made 40 families per acre the cheapest density).

The suitability of a density varies with the situation, the allowable cost, the habits of the group to be served, and the character of surrounding development. The site planner is not committed to a perfect number, but is sufficiently familiar with the implication of density to make a wise choice in a given situation or to avoid a building type or an activity inappropriate to a density fixed by some other consideration.

The density has other implications that belong to the sphere of city planning. Here one must consider the over-all pattern of a city: not simply the amenity of the site itself, but also the economy, function, social organization, and amenity of the city as a whole. While beyond the scope of site planning, it must be recognized that such considerations will often set densities at points in some conflict with what might be ideal when thinking of the site alone.

The site planner cultivates the habit of looking beyond the boundaries of his site to study the density and character of surrounding use and also to learn the place of the site in the larger patterns of the community as a whole. The preferred arrangement of use on the site may depend heavily on outside links, such as a movement to work, convenience to shopping or other facilities, or surrounding negative influences. The entire program may be reshaped by such off-site study. A hospital may decide to provide cooperative housing in the community at large rather than in on-site institutional dormitories, or a housing development may be able to add a swimming pool to be supported by a larger area. The site planner will as a matter of course refuse to accept the boundary lines he is given, whether they be lot lines, political boundaries, areas of study, or just the edges of a convenient map. He is not compelled to harmonize with these surroundings if they are undesirable or of doubtful longevity, but he must take them into account.

Most often the land use diagram indicates the final pattern to be achieved when construction is complete and the site fully occupied. Frequently, however, development will be a lengthy process, and partial occupation will occur before it is complete. Construction may occur in a series of jumps with periods of undisturbed use in between. In this case, it is necessary to prepare a set of diagrams showing stages in the plan, to see that each stage is workable in itself, and that each successive one develops logically out of its predecessor.

Local Siting Versus General Pattern

In developing a land use pattern through diagrams of use and linkages, scaled by density, there are two basic approaches that usually must both be used. The first is the placement of use according to detailed consideration of the accidents of site, or through small-scale ideas of use or form. Such a plan locates tall buildings where there is a fine distant view, row houses on a sunny slope, playlots at neighborhood focal points, and a park on some picturesque piece of terrain. The plan tends to have a chaotic look on paper, but has a rich, if disorganized, content when applied to the ground.

Alternatively, the pattern may be developed as a logical total organization of the uses and their linkages, with some general visual form in mind. This will look clear on paper, and be ordered and efficient in function. But it will smother the site, and disregard many small connections.

Usually both patterns are developed, and then by a long process of trial and criticism they are reshaped until a new pattern is discovered that has the values of both: one that responds to the details of site activity, and still expresses a clear general form. This is likely to be a difficult process, since no law of nature requires that a general form be inherent in any given situation, and human ingenuity is required to develop one.

The detailed approach is usually the easier one to accomplish, although it requires careful reconnaissance and painstaking meditation over the potentialities of each activity and of each piece of ground. It proceeds through a step-by-step chain of reconnaissance, detailed analysis of difficulties and possibilities, and then the assignment of uses. In this sense, a design concerned with a picturesque, demanding site or a traditional way of life is simpler than one dealing with flat or characterless ground, where limits, potentialities and differentiations must be developed by the designer himself.

The detailed approach has a motto: an appropriate use for each site, and an appropriate site for each use. It is tested by an item-by-item check, to see that all functions are housed with adequate quantity and quality of space, and that each advantage of the ground has been utilized, with no waste space. (Of course, what is commonly called "waste space" may have its own function, as will be seen).

Land Use Patterns

The general pattern approach is somewhat more difficult because it is abstract. Very often, a general pattern is never consciously considered, but only unconsciously assumed. An unconscious assumption normally results in the use of a very conventional pattern. When a general pattern *is* explicitly drawn, it very often is equally conventional, such as the typical symmetrical hierarchy or the balanced axis. These pattern habits are extremely difficult to break. It may prove that these conventional forms are indeed the best in a given situation, but that cannot be assumed until they are tested against other kinds of grouping.

Therefore the planner must develop his capacity to imagine alternative general forms, and be alert to see new ones in the world about him. A set of archetypal forms and a sense of their nature is part of his professional stock in trade.

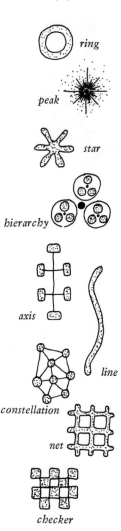

ring

peak

star

hierarchy

axis

line

constellation

net

checker

Page 11

Some examples of these general forms are the ring, the concentric peak, the radial star, the symmetric hierarchy, the axis, the line, the constellation of clusters, the network, the checkerboard.

The intrinsic formal character of each of these patterns has certain functional implications, such as rigidity or flexibility, dispersed or concentrated communication, specialization or repetition of parts. Other characteristics appear only when applied to a particular situation. These patterns once applied can be judged on many counts, but most likely two will be crucial: the accessibility provided between units, which is basic to the functioning of the whole; and the sense of form and organization that will be conferred on the final design, which is fundamental to its esthetic quality.

These general forms may be differentiated according to their characteristics of district pattern (shape of the boundary between development and nondevelopment, or the way the internal parts are arranged in sectors, checkers, stripes, or rings); focal pattern (arrangements of the intensive focal points of use or form); and network pattern (grid, radioconcentric, linear, capillary, and so on). We may discuss the density of development, or its grain (that is, the extent to which activities or forms are differentiated, how finely these differing classes are mixed, and how sharp the transition is between them). If, for example, we are putting together two different kinds of houses, then the grain of that mixture may be fine or coarse, and the transition between groups may be sharp or blurred.

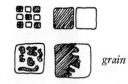

grain

Pattern and Objectives

The land use pattern of a development has much to do with its efficiency, its cost, its look, and its social workings. Some illustrations of these effects can be made in terms of the general objectives listed in Chapter 2. If, for example, we wish to promote social interaction between neighboring people, one effective device, given a homogeneous group, or other dimensions of the social environment which are favorable to intercourse, is to use common entrances and paths, to increase the visual contacts between paths and other locations such as house interiors, or to provide focal points, such as mail boxes, play yards, laundries, schools, churches,

FIGURE 6 *Children make their own worlds.*

or community centers. Sharp physical boundaries, on the other hand, will tend to divide people, and will be relatively unfrequented. A finer grain of residential type may encourage some communication between different kinds of people, but a coarser grain, with larger areas of homogeneity, will in all likelihood induce a greater total volume of communication, since interaction between similar people requires less effort. But if we want to allow residents to control the rate of communication, then we might see to it that each dwelling unit fronts upon an intensively used common area and zone of access, while the other side is as secluded and isolated as possible.

Individual choice is maximized by variety and fine grain of use and a rapid, controllable communication system. Plasticity and free play in an environment are enhanced by low density, and by a certain looseness in plan which leaves "waste areas" in which people can operate directly on their surroundings, and can grow and develop through such active intervention. Children can make their own worlds out of imagination and crude structures; adults can take the car apart, erect a shed, or plant a makeshift garden.

Adaptability to future change is favored by low density, by a good communication system, by a certain generality and standardization of form, and by separating the more permanent uses, or those which are physically more resistant to change, from the more temporary or easier to change activities. Cost is minimized by regularity of form, by compact arrangements, by minimizing expensive features such as roads, by using the highest density within the range desirable for the given use and structural type, and, of course, by reducing the standards of the facilities to be provided. These devices are dealt with in Chapter 14. Image quality, which depends so much on the clarity of plan and the nature of its sequential organization, is discussed in Chapter 5.

Page 236

Page 55

In any case, what is desired is a functioning unit, satisfying human desires in detail as well as on a broad scale. The designer must know the people who will inhabit his development; he must understand their wants and manner of life, or how he hopes to modify that manner of life. He must put himself in their place as best he can, and in imagination go through the actions that will characterize their activity there. What will it be like to mail a letter, talk to a neighbor, display wealth, dispose of trash, or seek adventure?

The land use diagram is a basic first step in the site plan, and deals in an efficient abstract way with many of the principal issues that must be resolved. But two final points must be made clear. Land use design is not a logical single-track process, proceeding inexorably from a knowledge of linkages to a final arrangement. Judgment and creative decision must be employed and many alternatives developed. Chapter 8 will give a better sense of the total site-planning process.

Page 115

Nor is the land use plan a separate entity, to be determined by itself. It is the Siamese twin of the circulation pattern, which will be discussed in the following chapter. Its implications for the physical, visual form must always be in mind, however tempting it may be to leave this question to a final period of architectural adornment. Will the site organization allow a clear expression of the principal functions? Will the arrangement of activities bring about a desirable visual effect? The principal danger of the land use method indeed lies in the tendency to think in terms of areal designations on paper, forgetting that what is being conceived is a form in three dimensions. Rough sketches of the concrete implications of land use proposals, concurrent development of the general visual form, and manipulation of the land use pattern on a model rather than on a map, may all help to overcome this danger.

Chapter 4

Systems of Circulation

Access is the prerequisite to the usefulness of any block of space. Without the ability to enter, leave, and move within it, to receive and transmit information or goods, space is of no value, however vast or rich in resource. A city or a large site can in fact be looked upon primarily as a communications net made up of roads, paths, rails, pipes, and wires. This system of flow is intimately related to the pattern of localized activities, or land use. The economic and cultural level of life is roughly in proportion to the capacity of the circulation system. The cost of the system is usually the most significant element in total site cost.

Flows can be of many different types: the movement of people, of goods, of wastes, or of information, carried in wheeled vehicles, on foot, on rails, in the air, in pipes or wires, or on endless belts; under, on, or above the surface. Even on the scale of a site plan it is important to think of these flows as a total system within which one element can often be substituted for another. Thus telephone calls or televised communications may substitute for personal trips, and the flow of gas in a pipe for the haulage of solid fuel. The layout of streets affects the pattern of underground utilities, and the location of telephone cable depends on the method being used to transmit power. It is in this domain that the site plan is the most sensitive to technological change.

The channel types in most common use today are the graded and surfaced rights-of-way for pedestrians or wheeled vehicles, the rail systems, the wires conveying power and information, the gravity flow sewers carrying off surface drainage and water-borne wastes, and the pressure pipes supplying such fluids as water, gas, steam, or even bulk materials in water suspension. Vehicular paths are normally laid on the surface and the pipes beneath it. Wires are placed underground or strung overhead.

Of all these the vehicular rights-of-way are likely to be the most critical in the plan. They convey persons as well as a variety of other objects, they are demanding of space and sensitive to alignment, and they are fundamental to the usefulness and quality of the locations that they border on. The other channels tend to be patterned in conformity with this dominant system. As a first approximation in design, it is usually possible to consider the layout of roads before that of the rest of the circulation system, and then to refine this layout by study of the other components.

Technical standards for roads are covered in Chapter 11

Among the utilities (the pipe and wire channels) it is the water supply that is likely to be most critical at the large community scale. The quantity, potability, and pressure of water available may exercise a serious check on development, or even forbid it. The disposal of sanitary sewage will also influence growth at the larger scale, especially when topography prohibits gravity flow to a good disposal point. But sewage disposal is becoming less of a determinant as the technique of small disposal plants improves.

At the local site planning scale neither water supply nor sewage disposal are likely to have a significant influence on the plan, while the management of surface drainage through the storm sewers may impose important modifications because of the size and cost of the storm sewer system, and the need to tie it into the natural drainage pattern of the area. Therefore it is likely to be the first utility network to be analyzed. The circulation considered in this case is not confined to the artificial channels. It is the flow of rain and melt water over the entire site, plus the off-site watershed, moving in sheets over the open ground, concentrating into ditches and swales, running then into the street gutters, entering the underground pipe system, and finally reaching the natural drainage lines of river, lake, or sea. Therefore the designer is concerned not only with the sewer system itself, but with the drainage of the ground surface, and its flooding and erosion.

See Chapter 12

The technique of underground circulation is in general rather backward in comparison to that of surface systems. Sub-surface structures are expensive and inelegant, their design highly empirical and traditional, the hidden layout chaotic to an extreme. This is painfully visible when a street is opened up or when such utilities are strung overhead.

In general, utility systems may be integrated or dispersed. That is, water may come through great aqueducts from a single metropolitan reservoir, or each house may have its own well; sewage may go to a central disposal plant or be disposed of in individual septic tanks; storm water may be diverted into local brooks and ponds or be carried in great collecting lines; electricity may be distributed on a regional grid or be furnished by individual generators, and so on. The choice between extremes, or the many half-way stations between, is dictated by the circumstances of density, topography, custom, and available facilities. But it is more usual to use centralized sources of electricity for economy and reliability, and a central water supply for reasons of public health. Storm drainage systems, on the other hand, are usually as dispersed as possible.

Distribution lines may also be differentiated in another way. There are the systems in which materials, energy or information are conveyed under "pressure", some external applied force. These systems include the water, gas, electricity, and telephone lines. Here the channels are small in cross section, continuous, flexible, flowing full, typically fitted with valves and subject to frequent breaks. Their pattern will usually appear as a large interconnected network or web. Then there are systems in which materials flow by gravity, the storm and sanitary sewers in particular. These must be laid carefully to consistent slopes; they are rigid, jointed, relatively large, typically flowing only partially full. Finally there are the channels along which objects move by self-propulsion: the roads, rails, and air lanes.

Despite the variety of type and constant innovation, physical circulation has certain general characteristics which seem to be stable. When the quantity of flow is more than insignificant, it must be organized in defined channels with terminals and interchanges. These channels are then organized into networks, which distribute the flows over large areas. This is true not only of roads or pipes, but of footways, wires, and air lanes as well. The greater the flow, the greater the necessary definition, control, and specialization of the channel, with more elaborate terminals and interchanges, and with the total trip from origin to destination becoming more indirect, though not necessarily more inefficient. Superhighways are an example of this tendency.

Patterns of Channels

These networks of channels may take one of several general forms. Very often they occur as a uniform grid which may be either rectangular or triangular. The seldom-encountered triangular grid produces more difficult intersections, but gives straight travel in three instead of two directions and so comes closer to providing uniform access. A hexagonal or triangular grid may be used for a local street system but at a small scale tends to produce awkward sites for development.

Grids in general are useful where flows are shifting and broadly distributed. Although generalized, they are clear and easy to follow. They are well suited to networks serving complex areas at large scales. The rectangular grid is still the system more commonly used for patterns of local streets. It has been criticized for its visual monotony, for its disregard of topography, for its vulnerability to through traffic, and for its lack of differentiation between heavily travelled and lightly travelled ways, which prevents specialized design and the economical use of space and paving.

These criticisms are not inherent in the pattern itself but in its particular use. Heavy or through traffic can be directed on to particular lines of the grid, and monotony can be avoided by the variation of the building and landscape pattern. The grid may be curved to fit topography or to discourage through movement. The essence of a grid system is in its general sense of direction, its sequence of lines, and its regularity of interconnection. It need not be composed of geometrically straight lines nor must it enclose blocks of equal size and shape.

The grid may be modified by controlling the traffic flow through it. For example, all flows may be made one-way, alternating in direction between one line and the next parallel one. Capacities will increase and intersections will be simplified with most of the conflicting maneuvers eliminated. But it requires more forethought and a lengthier journey, to move through the system. An extreme example of this type is the so-called "steady-flow system," in which movement is directed clockwise and counterclockwise around adjacent blocks, so that flow in any one channel is one-way, but reverses its direction between each intersection. There are no direct crossings, only weaving movements, as on a rotary. The system may work for small-scale access networks where flows are heavy, but it makes any continuous trip exceedingly indirect.

Blocked grids are a further refinement. In order to direct through traffic and to allow the differentiation of paths, occasional interruptions are made in the grid leaving the whole pattern intact. This system will often take a swastika form.

The grid pattern has the definite advantages of simplicity, convenient access, good orientation, and suitability for complex distributed flow. On level or moderately rolling land it may be a very good solution. Its familiar faults are primarily due to poor application.

Another general form is the radial system, in which channels spread out from a center. This system is particularly appropriate where flows have a common origin, interchange, or destination, such as a single water source or sewage disposal point, a central telephone exchange, a common workplace to which commutation is destined, or even a symbolic center such as a royal palace. The radial system gives the most direct line of travel for such centrally directed flows, although at high levels of traffic the central terminus becomes difficult to handle. It is a relatively rigid system in comparison to the grid and does not respond easily to shifts in the central activity, nor does it work well if some flows have neither origin nor destination in the center. Rings may be added to the system to make a radioconcentric net, which still favors central flow but allows bypassing movements as well. This may work well where the central flow is still predominant. In its outer reaches and at a large scale this net acts like a rectangular grid. A radial system of local streets was once highly regarded, but it is now rarely used since it causes problems in local flow and creates difficult building sites.

A further modification of the radial system is to allow branchings at other points than the center itself. This is the classic pattern, in nature as well as in design, of central distribution or collection. It is commonly seen in water, power, and sewage systems. It allows the most direct line of travel, favors the specialization of major versus minor arteries, and makes the intersection problem manageable by distributing intersections instead of concentrating them at the center. Otherwise, the branching system has the general difficulties

of the radial type, being especially frustrating to noncentral flow. Thus the use of dead-end streets in residential layouts permits lightly built, safe, minor streets, but creates difficulties for emergency or delivery vehicles. Any branching system is also very sensitive to interruptions at single points on the main lines, whether it be a broken water main or an arterial occlusion in the human body.

There is a third general circulatory pattern: the linear system. It may consist of a single line or a parallel series. This system is particularly useful where flows run between two points rather than to or from a single point. In addition, since all activities are grouped along the line, all subsidiary flows also have direct lines of travel. It is an economical form when the first cost of the channel is high but terminal cost is low, and when there is little saving to be gained by building branches for lower capacities. Since there are no intersections, frontage along the channel is used to its maximum. Thus the linear system is typically seen in developments along freight railroads, canals, or trolley car lines, in pioneer agricultural areas where road cost is relatively high, and in strip development along highways. Its disadvantages are its lack of focus and the overloading of the channel that may easily occur because of the innumerable on-and-off movements along its length.

At the site-planning scale the system may appear as linear settlements or "roadtowns," or may be used in conformity with the limitations of some linear site along a water or topographic edge. The linear pattern may be modified by specializing it into channels which take through movements and others which take the local flows: a spinal main street bordered or intersected by minor ways. Another system connects minor loops on alternate sides of a major way, so that two continuous paths are provided, one major and direct, the other local and sinuous.

Closing the line upon itself to form a loop improves the characteristics of flow by giving two choices of direction to each destination. With one or two inlets added this becomes a loop distribution system, which is generally preferable to the branching radial for the distribution of electricity or water. Similarly, a minor residential street which comes off the main artery as a loop rather than a dead end is the more efficient unless the cul-de-sac is very short. Here the loop allows alternate exits, as well as continuous progressive movement for service circulation.

Sometimes a deliberate disorder of local streets may be created to discourage through movement, to adjust to intricate topography, or to create interest in the street picture. This disorder need not cause waste of land or excessive street frontage. It can be justifiable on difficult terrain where the ground form, rather than the streets, will give a sense of pattern. It may also be used in small areas, enclosed with a more rational layout, to give a sense of intimacy, mystery, or special character. But if continued over areas of any size, such a scheme becomes confusing and exasperating.

Just as in the case of the general forms of activity pattern, these general circulation forms are worth knowing as alternatives. They need not be geometrically pure, and are of course modified by the external influences of land use or topography. Whatever system is chosen, it should be obvious that it must fit into the general pattern of the larger region of which the development is a part.

Compare with the activity forms on page 34

Alignment

Defined channels usually have a characteristic and fairly consistent cross section located along a continuous centerline. This centerline must have a definite location in three-dimensional space, an *alignment*, which is usually analyzed for design convenience into a horizontal and a vertical component. Each type of channel has its own requirements for these two alignments, depending on the expected speed, volume, and nature of flow. Standards tend to shift from time to time and place to place, as technology, climate, or culture changes.

A common difficulty in site planning concerns the size and rigidity of these alignment standards, which are in conflict with the relative fluidity and irregularity of landscape. It requires considerable skill to make a major road seem to "flow" with the land, to arrange a harmonious joint between a tree and a telephone pole, or to grade the land smoothly between a driveway and a sloping garden. While alignments are detailed and formalized only toward the end of the planning process, the designer is thinking in terms of their requirements as he sketches the circulation system in his preliminary layout.

Figure 8, page 47

Alignment characteristics are basic information for a site planner, despite their tendency to change with technology. However convenient the division into channel types

and alignment components may be, the designer considers each line as a three-dimensional unit, and thinks of it in relation to the system as a whole.

Grain and Interchange

A recurring issue in the design of circulation systems is that of grain: the degree of specialization of flow, and the fineness with which it is applied. Greater flows can be accommodated with safety if pedestrians and cars travel on their own systems. Efficiency will also go up when one sorts out trucks, bicycles, children, idle strollers, and so on. It is advantageous to put fast, long-distance traffic in special channels of its own, separate from slow local flow. The advantage lies both in the efficiency of homogeneous flow and the savings which can be realized in being able to build channels designed for a more restricted purpose, such as allowing light pavements on minor streets.

On the other hand, each gain in specialization is a loss in flexibility; it becomes more difficult to change from one mode of transportation to another, and paths are more indirect. The system is likely to be more complex and more difficult to change as need arises. If, for example, trucks, cars, and pedestrians are all separated in a residential area, then trips will be longer and require better orientation, the system will require frequent grade separations, and each dwelling will require three entrances. Our expensive superhighway systems, running in their own special rights-of-way and requiring massive engineering structures, have markedly increased capacity and speed for a particular type of flow. Should this type of circulation lose its dominant importance, this specialized system may become a serious obstacle to a readaptation of the environment. As another example of specialization, a one-way traffic system speeds flow but makes it more difficult to reach a given destination. Large superblocks, which increase the grain between the circulatory and noncirculatory zones, improve the amenity of the living areas at the price of frustrating through traffic.

Figure 8, page 47

The superblock is a large piece of developable land surrounded by a continuous street. As a result of its size, the surrounding street system is as indirect as is tolerable. The block is often curved or kidney-shaped to fit the topography. The size of the block may be further increased by the use of culs-de-sac or minor loops, which penetrate inward without dividing the block: superblocks as large as 50 acres

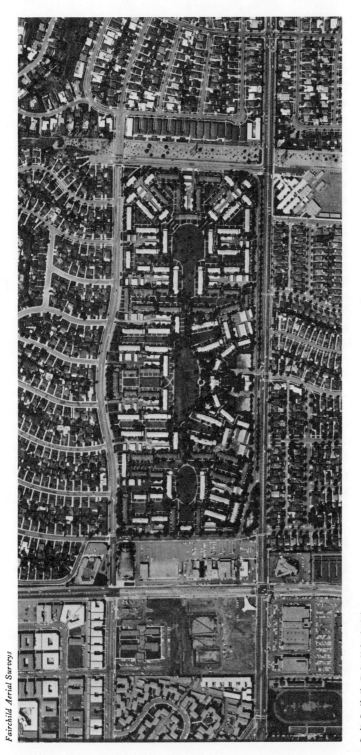

FIGURE 7 *Air view of Baldwin Hills, Los Angeles, classic example of the superblock. Designed by Henry Wright and Clarence Stein, the interior is devoted to a common park. Note the variation in pattern of the surrounding residential development.*

within the bounding rights-of-way are not impossible. By eliminating street intersections, this technique minimizes expensive street frontage per unit. It tends to concentrate through traffic, keeping loads light on the minor streets. Large and relatively inexpensive interior parks can be provided. If interior footways are included, pedestrians can move substantial distances without crossing a street.

Originally it was thought that pedestrian and motor access could be completely separated within these blocks, but experience has shown that the loop or cul-de-sac street, the point of motor access, is also used as the principal foot entrance to the units about it. It attracts most of the pedestrian flow, much of the close-to-home play activity of the children, and becomes the social focus. Therefore it is important to provide a link between it and the main walkway system within the superblock, while the common walks giving access to the rear of the units may often be dispensed with.

At the residential scale at least, complete dissociation of foot and vehicular travel now seems neither necessary nor desirable, except for the traditional separation of street and bordering sidewalks. But major walkways that cut across long blocks or pass through their landscaped interiors at some distance from the streets, walks that carry substantial numbers of pedestrians, are very desirable as additions to the normal street and sidewalk channels. These separate walkways must be adequately maintained, policed, and lighted. Even the sidewalks along the streets need not follow the road alignment slavishly but can merge and diverge in response to minor accidents of terrain, in consonance with the nature of pedestrian movement. Sidewalks are play areas as well as foot paths, and are an essential element in most site plans.

Superblocks impose a more and more circuitous path on local traffic as their size increases. If no internal walks are provided because of problems of maintenance and control, then movement on foot can become very difficult. For this reason there are certain commonly accepted maxima for the lengths of blocks, culs-de-sac, and loop streets, which are quoted in Chapter 11. Some of the disadvantages of long culs-de-sac may be mitigated by interconnecting their ends by foot paths, water-line easements, or emergency service roads: in other words, by converting them into loops for special purposes. For facilitating circulation and social in-

Page 180

tercourse, there are distinct advantages in keeping block lengths short, particularly where flows are less intensive and disruptive.

Thus there are always pressures both to increase and decrease the grain of circulation, and the proper balance depends on the particular situation. Most likely, the best solution will provide high specialization at centers where flow is intense, grading to low specialization where flow is small: using freeways at one end of the system, for example, and a graveled walking-driving-parking-play area at the other. In a total system, however, some hierarchy of channels is likely to be needed. The conventional hierarchy of urban streets begins with the loop, cul-de-sac, or minor street which gives access to the low-intensity uses fronting on them. The minor streets lead to the collector where local centers are located, but on which uses such as houses may still front. The collector empties into the major arterial, built for heavy flows, with intersections at longer intervals, intensive fronting uses, and access controlled but not excluded. Any low-intensity use on an arterial will front on to an intervening service road. From the arterial one enters the freeway, with widely spaced grade-separated intersections and no fronting access.

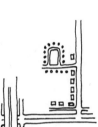

Another persistent problem of the circulation system is that of interchanges and terminals. The problem appears when the elements of flow are individually oriented, i.e., when a given car or telephone message must reach a par-

FIGURE 8 *A portion of the Central Artery in Boston. The rigidly specialized expressway, with its demanding alignment, slashes through the old city fabric.*

Nishan Bichajian

ticular destination. It becomes acute where flows are intense and channels specialized. Here the stopping and shifting that occurs throughout a nonspecialized line is visibly concentrated at the point of interchange. The delays and conflicts at these points tend to become the chief losses in the system, as evidenced by the notorious terminal time of the air lines. The growth of these difficulties may call a halt to further specialization or cause decentralization so as to distribute and scale down the termini.

A typical contemporary puzzle is how best to enter a building when arriving by car. There are functional problems of deceleration, and of entry and storage capacity. There are esthetic problems of a change of scale, and a danger of isolating the entrance behind a forecourt of parked cars. There must be a visual transition between velocity and repose; both driver and pedestrian must be oriented and aware of what they are approaching. All this requires a surprisingly large area of ground. It may be desirable for the car to pass close to the entrance before parking, after which its passengers approach the same entrance a second time on foot. Parking may be dispersed, placed in separate levels, or threaded with lines of activity or landscaping that afford an inviting access to the principal destination.

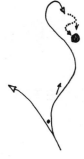

Capacities and Costs

For capacities of roads and utilities, see Chapters 11 and 12

The maximum capacity of a channel, in vehicles, or persons, messages, or cubage per hour, is an important measure of its ability to perform its function. In the road system it is usually the intersections and intakes that are the bottlenecks, and their capacity is the limiting factor. In time we will be able to analyze simultaneously the capacity of a total system of roads, as we now can do for a water supply network or an electrical power net. Road systems also produce serious problems of terminal storage or parking, since the carriers are large compared to the object carried, are individually operated, and are idle much of the time. Parking at times becomes a problem insoluble by site-planning means alone.

The circulation system is the most expensive feature of site development, and its layout has significant cost implications. A few general rules may be stated for reducing this cost. The first is simply to minimize the length of channel per using activity. This requires a minimum number of intersections, each of which requires length that cannot be developed as frontage, and continuous development on both sides of the line with minimum frontage per unit. A heavily developed endless single line is the cheapest layout from this point of view and increasing the size of blocks approximates it. An exception to this rule occurs when roads on very steep land run parallel to the contours: in this case, it may be so difficult to connect development on the lower side with the road and its utilities that it is cheaper to develop only one side of the path.

Secondly, it is usually cheaper to specialize, short of the point where elaborate interchanges are needed. Thus a plan with arteries and minor streets will be less expensive than an undifferentiated grid. Thirdly, it is usually cheaper to lay out channels so that they have gentle gradients and no more than gentle curves. Sharp curves, steep grades, and flat grades all increase costs due to earthwork and special features.

The road layout also has a decisive effect on the development potential of the land, not only in the way the roads confer access, but also in the shape of the plots that remain: the holes in the net. Other things being equal, the larger and more regular these plots are, and the nearer their corners approximate right angles, the easier they are to develop for any purpose.

A road lying along the contours permits level foundations for buildings fronting on it, but if the cross slope is sharp, then access to these buildings may be labored, sewers difficult to reach, and the visual space lopsided. In this case it may be necessary to widen the right-of-way to take up the cross slope and to dissociate the facing buildings visually, or it may be necessary to use separate utilities for the lower structures, or one-sided frontage, or special building types on the lower side which are entered at an upper story. For these reasons, contour-following roads should normally be kept back from the brow of a hill if double frontage is intended.

Roads perpendicular to the contours avoid these problems, although foundations must now be stepped (which is somewhat more expensive), and street and utility gradients may become too steep. Rear lots may have awkward cross slopes requiring substantial terracing but it may be possible to use special step-down building types in a dramatic way.

Roads diagonal to the contours produce plots which are the most difficult to use, and should be avoided except where slopes are gentle, or where they are so steep that neither parallel nor perpendicular roads will serve.

Social and Esthetic Impact of Circulation

If we now confine our attention to the channels along which people move, we find that there are two additional effects to be considered: social and esthetic. These effects occur wherever people go, and not only when they happen to be on foot. It is currently fashionable, in reaction to the American scene, to think of the pedestrian as being completely distinct from that mechanical monster, the car, a monster to be kept in tunnels and underground garages. But cars have drivers who are as human as the rest of us.

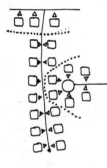

The path system affects communication between people. It appears that one prime way to encourage contacts between neighbors is to put them on a common pathway, with which their dwellings have frequent visual contact, and upon which their entrances visibly open. Friendships are made along the street rather than across the park. Contrariwise, the designer can foster privacy, division, or isolation by providing separate routes, masked routes such as apartment hallways, and doors not intervisible.

This effect extends upward in scale, so that a main street is often the heart of a community. As the scale of flow increases beyond this point, however, and particularly as the difficulty of crossing increases and as entrances no longer open directly upon it, then the path suddenly reverses its role and becomes a barrier rather than a main stem. Thus a crowded downtown street can be a center, while an expressway is a divisive wall. A cul-de-sac will focus a neighborhood group, while a broad planted parkway may delimit it. These effects can usually be inferred by going in imagination through routine movements and noting what casual contacts may thereby arise.

The pattern of streets or paths may provide or destroy the sense of focus or center in the plan, since persons in motion are oriented to the forward direction and a focussing of paths automatically gives the feeling of a strategic common point. Surprising effects of apparent association or disassociation with neighboring areas can be produced by connecting or disconnecting one local street system with another. Real estate developers are well aware of this and usually seek to attach their roads to those of the "best" districts in their vicinity.

Ogden Tanner, Architectural Forum

FIGURE 9 *Neighborly talk along a common walkway in Chatham Village, Pittsburgh, one of the most skillfully designed row house developments in the United States (Henry Wright and Clarence Stein, again).*

The pathways are the locus of points from which the development will be seen. They therefore have a profound effect on the visual character of the whole. They should have a clearly ordered system of their own, without ambiguities, and should expose the image of the whole development in as clear a way as possible. Along them the traveller should experience a pleasant sequence of space and form, and they should be expressive of the function and nature of the site. The path system is one of the most powerful means of making clear the underlying topography, whether by running submissively with the contours, or by aggressively opposing them.

In sketching the system of roads and paths it must be remembered that they will be seen as sharply foreshortened objects in perspective, and not as patterns from the air. Minor deviations will appear significant, pronounced curves will seem startlingly abrupt, and complex patterns will be incomprehensible. The pathways should seem to go fairly directly to their destination, and changes in direction should appear reasonable. It may at times be necessary to introduce artificial obstacles of terrain or structure or to mask possible short cuts.

There is some conflict, particularly in residential areas, between the functional desirability of a continuous network, and the visual pleasure in terminals and bounded spaces. The long straight street will seem to go nowhere, and even the curving layout, although blocking the "infinite" view, becomes wearying as the endless curves pass by. For this reason, it may be advisable to use "T" junctions on minor streets, with an important structure on the axis. The latter system will be very irritating, however, if it is used beyond the minor street level, and may bring about a chaotic structure even here if employed over too wide an area. Other techniques include the opening and closing of building or planting lines, to make visual compartments along a continuous road, and the use of more definite direction changes, with important objects at the break to act as visual termini.

The character of the line depends on the speed and manner with which it is traversed. A footpath responds nervously to minor changes in terrain and is adorned with intimate spaces and outlooks, while a highway will take a sweeping line and pass through simple and expansive spaces. Pedestrian motion, like a flow of water, has an apparent fluid momentum. It follows lines of least resistance, shortening distance by cut-offs. It swings wide on curves, eddies about obstacles, forms pools above and below restricted channels such as stairs or corridors. The flow may be smooth or turbulent, purposeful or meandering. It can be deflected or encouraged by visual attractions, by levels, openings, or the character of the floor. Only with difficulty can it be blocked. As a fine highway expresses the geometry of vehicular movement, so an adequate walk system reflects the characteristics of motion of foot.

Because of the prevalent ugliness of much of our circulation equipment, it is normal to consider roads and utilities as regretfully necessary things that must be supplied but should be hidden. Electric lines are put underground, parking areas planted out, and roads decked over. Yet since the flow system is one of the two basic attributes of a developed site and has much to do not only with its usefulness but with its interest and meaning as well, we should demand an even clearer expression of the essential elements of this system, instead of camouflaging them. Power lines and highways can be a powerful and beautiful component of the landscape.

The detailed standards of layout for walks, roads, and utilities are dealt with in Chapters 11 and 12. It is usual to begin with the walks and streets, since they have the most critical effect, and to check the other utilities later. The system is designed together with the visual form and the land use pattern, and its influence on these two is reviewed constantly. Studies devoted solely to circulation may be made, especially at an early stage, but these will be done only to develop a sense of the situation. No design decisions can be reached except with sketches or models which show use, flow, and form all together as an operating whole. All these features are usually brought up, via many alternatives, to a detailed sketch stage, and then the engineering of the flow system is investigated to see what modifications may be required.

Pages 176 and 192

In the analysis of site plans, whether as a part of the design process, or in the review of someone else's plan, the circulation system should be tested in every dimension. Does the system acquit its required function of transportation: can the necessary movements be accomplished along it at acceptable standards of time, cost, and safety? A plan of streets and walks should always be checked by mentally making the routine trips and noting their nature. While automobile movements may be provided for in detail, there is a tendency to neglect movement on foot. How does one get from car to house, and what is this approach like? How do children walk to school, or adults to a bus or to shopping? How does one get access to a building or a site for repair and maintenance? The check should be quantitative as well: can the particular channels carry the amount of flow desired? As our knowledge develops, we will proceed from the checking of single channels to the quantitative analysis of entire networks.

The plan should also be criticized to see if the right balance of specialization has been struck and if the interchanges and terminals are workable. It must be tested for cost, particularly for the length per using activity and the presence of special features. It should be checked to see that the parcels remaining for development are good ones, suited to the use proposed and capable of adjustment to other use. The social consequences of the path system can be analyzed in the light of the designer's objectives. The visual impact of the circulation must also be evaluated, particularly for the sequence of views that will be presented to the traveller.

The circulation system may finally be judged as a totality. Is the general pattern one which is suitable for the basic task? Will it seem orderly and well oriented to someone on the ground? Can it be abstracted, as a differentiated system, into a basic structure of main lines on which are dependent a set of subsidiary lines? Do its regions of high capacity coincide with the foci of activity? Is its structure coherent with the structure of use? Is it in balance with the intensity of activity, neither overwhelming nor being overwhelmed? As a total system, will it help to express site and function? Does it connect smoothly with the surrounding systems?

The circulation system is most prone to technological development, and therefore must be most adaptable to future change. If a self-contained water and sewage purification cycle for the individual unit becomes economical, as it is now technically feasible, then it may become unnecessary to tie a building to an underground water and sewage system. If future land vehicles will hover over the ground on compressed air, rather than rolling on wheels, then road characteristics will be revised. If urban areas are to be roofed with vast, light spans, then surface drainage loses its significance. Certainly there will be many less radical innovations which will at least modify the design of circulation systems. It is for this reason that, in the balance of analysis, such general considerations as pattern, the degree of specialization, and the social and visual impact are likely to have more weight than precise technical standards.

Chapter 5

Visual Form

A setting will convey either clarity or ambiguity, meaning or senselessness, stimulus or monotony, pleasure or disgust. The sensuous function is as important as the demands of circulation or of use. Its requirements may not coincide with technical demands and a solution must be found which satisfies each of them, or sacrifices them all to an equal degree.

Most people understand this when arranging a living room, but will ignore it in the arrangement of a site plan. We are attentive to the technical features, but pass over their integration into a visual whole. It is as though we were concerned with the amount of furniture to be put in a room, but let the movers put it down at will.

What we require is a *landscape*, technically organized so that its parts work together, but visually coherent as well, and whose visual image is congruent with its life and action. This concept of landscape as a visual and functional whole is a relatively recent one in Western culture. Such a whole in nature is the mature stage of development, shaped by the consistent impact of well-balanced forces. In art it is the result of comprehensive purpose skillfully applied. The visual success of man-made landscape depends upon clarity and decisiveness of intent even more than does its technical success.

In its essence, the sensuous experience of a site is a spatial one, a perception of the volume of air which surrounds the observer, appreciated principally but not entirely through the eyes. While this outdoor space, like architectural space, is made palpable by light and is defined by enclosure — overhead, alongside, and underfoot — yet it has peculiar characteristics of its own. These characteristics have fundamental implications for the art of site planning.

In contrast to architectural space, site space is much larger in extent and looser in form. The horizontal dimensions are normally much greater than the vertical dimensions. Structure is less geometric or demanding, connections less precise, shapes more irregular. Even in a formal city square, an irregularity in plan which would be unbearable in a room may at the exterior scale be tolerable or even desirable.

The site plan uses different materials, notably earth, rock, water, and plants, and is subject to constant change, whether it be the rhythm of human activity and of the natural cycles, or the cumulative effects of growth, decay, and alteration. The light which gives it form shifts constantly with weather, hour, and season. Most important of all, it is seen, not as a single view, but in sequence over an extended period of time while the observer himself is in motion.

All these differences call for corresponding differences in design technique. The looseness of outdoor space and the difficulty that all but highly trained eyes have in estimating distance, geometry of plan, level or gradient, allow a certain freedom or even indifference in a layout. Many formal flaws can be masked, and optical illusions achieved: two bodies of water coalesce because their outlines seem to match, a large object "disappears" when blocked out by a small object nearby, an axis appears straight which is bent in reality. Level areas may appear to tilt by contrast with adjacent counter slopes, or the relative elevations of objects may be seemingly reversed by the treatment of the grades surrounding them.

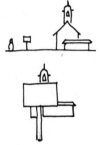

This freedom to create illusion carries with it a responsibility to produce a clear and connected whole. A simple, readable, well-proportioned space in the outdoors is an event of great power. Basic structure must be visually explained in a way that purely natural forces rarely accomplish; structural and symbolic connections that defy distance must be established. The dimensions that in their raw state are difficult to grasp should be made legible by the use of roads, trees, or other measuring devices; the connection of part with whole intimated by symbolic echoes of shape or material.

The designer uses every resource to confirm the form he intends to establish. Except in special cases where he attempts an air of mystery and doubt, he makes sure that his spaces are well defined, unambiguous in form, and clearly joined at well-marked transitions. If the space is to have rhythm and directed movement, then that rhythm and direction will be supported by the form of all visible elements. Changes in plan must coordinate with changes in section.

Spatial dimensions are reinforced by light, color, texture, and detail. The eye judges distance by many optical features, and some of these can be manipulated to exaggerate or diminish apparent depth: the overlapping of more distant objects by closer ones; the parallactic movement of objects disposed in depth; the expectation that farther things will be higher above the base line; the smaller size and finer texture of things far away; the apparent bluish color of distant surfaces; the convergence of parallel lines. Used with restraint, these manipulations add to the spatial effect. As with any illusion, there is a danger that from another viewpoint or in another season the trick will be exposed. Illusions of features indirectly perceived, such as geometric plan, distance, or level, are the easiest to achieve and maintain. Illusions of characteristics seen directly, such as the attempt to imitate the color and texture of one material in a substitute, are much more difficult and questionable.

Outdoor spaces are rarely created by complete enclosure, but rather partially, by the conformation of the floor and by smaller vertical elements which suggest imaginary aerial definitions. Since the out-of-doors is dominantly horizontal, vertical features or changes take on exaggerated importance. A gentle gradient or a slight rise in level may change the scene radically. A hill, which in fact occupies only a very small vertical angle in the visual field, seems much higher. The photograph of an apparently awesome mountain landscape shows only a minor disturbance of the horizon.

Steep slopes or drops are usually difficult to handle within a regularly organized space: it is a safe rule to take up such vertical differences in the approach to, or between, important openings. Level changes may be used to define space by themselves, and they add many additional visual possibilities, whether of view, silhouette, truncation, or dynamic movement. The general plan shape of a site may often bear less on the visual success of the whole than the smaller refinements of projection, level, or form which make the real visual space on the ground.

Once a readable space is established, it has a strong emotional impact on the observer. The intimacy or constraint conveyed by a small enclosed space, and the exhilaration or awe of a great opening, are both universal sensations. Even stronger is a transition between the two: the powerful sense of contraction or release.

Spaces differ in character according to their shape and their intrinsic proportions (ratio of height to width to length). Proportion is relative and may be studied in a model, but spaces are also judged in absolute terms by their scale with respect to objects outside of themselves. Outdoor en-

FIGURE 10 *The vast space of Central Park, New York City.*

closures, for example, must contend with the vast scale of the sky, and a plan either makes a transition between its own size and that of the earth's atmosphere (by large openings or the use of verticals), or it chooses to shut out the sky, and to reduce it to a backdrop.

A relation to the scale of the surrounding landscape, rural or urban, must also be established, and a choice of isolation or integration must again be made. One of the most exacting tasks of site planning is to fit substantial new additions into a mature and established landscape in such a way that the new functions and structures can be absorbed without disrupting the old scale, the previous rhythm and balance. Finally, a space has a scale with respect to the observer himself, and either appears in touch with him and measurable by him, or takes on an awesome and superhuman size. In

Reference 2

FIGURE 11 *The narrow, rich, intensely human space of a Florentine street (the Borgo Allegri).*

each case, the scale relationship should be decisively intended and decisively carried out.

A few tentative quantities can be assigned to the size and proportion of external spaces. Although developed empirically in the course of direct observations outdoors, these statements seem to derive from the optical characteristics of the human eye, and from the size of the objects which are generally of greatest interest to it, i.e., other human beings. We can detect a man about 4000 feet away, recognize him at 80 feet, see his face as a clear portrait at 45 feet, and feel him to be in direct relation to us, whether pleasant or intrusive, at 3 to 10 feet. Outdoor spaces of the latter dimension seem extremely or intolerably small, while dimensions of 40 feet appear intimate. Those up to 80 feet are felt to be still at an easy human scale. Most of the successful enclosed squares of the past have not exceeded 450 feet, at least in the smaller dimension. There are few good urban vistas much over a mile in length, unless they are distant panoramas seen over a featureless foreground, such as views over water or from high places.

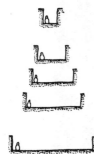

Moreover there are limits to the angle of clear vision and to the rapidity of scanning, so that an object whose major dimension equals its distance from the eye is difficult to see as a whole, but tends to be analyzed in detail. When it is twice as far away as its major dimension, then it appears clearly as a whole; when it is thrice as far, it is still dominant in the visual field but is seen in relation to other objects. As the distance increases beyond four times the major dimension, the object simply becomes one part of the general scene. Thus it is often said that an external enclosure is most comfortable when its walls are one-half or one-third as high as the width of the space enclosed, while if the ratio falls below one-fourth, the space ceases to seem enclosed. If the walls are higher than the width, then one does not see the skyline nor easily judge the wall's height. The space becomes a pit or trench. These rules assume viewing positions near the edge of the space, and the intent to produce comfortable yet clearly bounded areas. In other situations other proportions may be preferred.

As another example of an esthetic standard based on human anatomy, we find that it is unpleasant if the line of sight just at eye level is an ambiguous one. The ambiguity may be caused by a narrow visual barrier at that level, or by a vertical surface terminating there. Preferably, vision is either kept clear at this sensitive elevation, or is decisively blocked.

Thus walls should be low, or over six feet high, and railings at eye level are to be avoided.

Spaces may be enclosed by opaque barriers, or by walls which are semitransparent or broken by gaps or windows. The space definers may be visual suggestions rather than physical stops: colonnades, bollards, changes in ground pattern, imaginary extensions of objects. The traditional enclosers of urban space have been the buildings themselves, but this enclosure has become more difficult to accomplish as the demand for open areas around buildings has grown, particularly for transportation facilities. To some extent these breaks in enclosure may be masked by such devices as staggered streets, building overlaps or bridging buildings, the addition of screen walls or colonnades, or even the continuous lines of walk and low fence, as in a colonial New England street. Enclosure may also be achieved by planting, or, perhaps more rationally, the spatial effect sought may be modified to fit the new conditions.

Spaces vary in effect by the way in which they are entered, passed through, and left behind, and by the related spaces that precede and follow them. Their appearance is modified by the activity that goes on within their confines, by the color and texture of walls and floor, by the way in which they are lighted, and by the objects and details with which they are furnished. Wall Street on a Sunday morning and Wall Street during the weekday lunch hour are quite different spaces; a familiar square can change mysteriously under artificial light. An empty room is notoriously smaller than that same room with furniture; distances seem much shorter over open, empty water. A scale relation between a man and a vast space can be established by the use of a few "man-sized" objects; a tall object may relate a small space to the larger world. Blue or grey walls strengthen the atmospheric perspective, and thus seem farther away. Surfaces of hot strong color come closer. Downhill views are apparently long, and uphill views foreshortened.

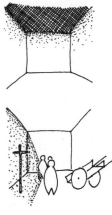

Since space is primarily sensed by vision, the direction and quality of the light which bathes that space is a determinant of its character. Light will sharpen or blur definitions, emphasize the silhouette or texture, conceal or reveal a feature, contract or expand dimensions. The outlines of silhouetted objects are very prominent visual features, and the designer is always careful of objects which will appear against the sky. He is also aware of the apparent outward radiation of bright surfaces, so that light sources seem en-

larged, and silhouetted objects thin. Shadow patterns can be distinctive features, whether they are large masses or delicate traceries, dark and opaque or scintillating with light. Besides being used for effects of texture or spatial definition, shadows may be employed to focus attention or frame a view, or a long shadow may be directed so as to explain the modelling of a surface.

To some extent, the designer can manipulate outdoor light by casting shadows, orienting surfaces, or filtering light through screens. More often he is concerned with creating a form which will receive natural light gracefully, which will reveal itself to the hazy sun of winter and to the blaze of summer, which seems coherent in the morning and the evening alike, or under snow, rain, or bright moon. To do this, he must be aware of the geometry of sun and moon position, of the light effects of various weathers, and in particular he must be sensitive to that quality of light which is special to his locale and climate.

He has another resource in artificial light. Most developments are used at night as well as day, and some may be inhabited even more intensively after dark. Artificial light, in all its variation of color, direction, motion, and intensity, can produce a new visual world. Spaces can be modified or even created with light alone, planes be made to advance or recede, objects brought to the foreground, textures transformed, a new mood set. It is pleasant to look from darkness into light, or vice versa; to watch a rhythmical play of light patterns; or to see an object transformed by a steadily changing light source. This is a resource now almost unused.

Other senses besides vision help to convey the shape of a space. Most notable is the sense of hearing: nocturnal animals and the human blind depend on echo location in moving through the world. The character of a space is partly given to us by the quality of the noise reflected to our ears: an absence of echo, for example, being interpreted as openness. Similarly, though to a lesser extent, we are affected by the feel of a surface (or by how it looks as if it should feel), and by its radiation of heat to our skin, or vice versa. Thus the visual location of a wall may be substantially reinforced if it is highly reflective to sound, looks rough to touch, or radiates heat. All these characteristics of light, sound, and touch may be consciously used by the designer to support his main intent.

Certain space forms and their furnishings have symbolic connotations that seem to be common to our culture: the awesomeness of great size and simple form, and the pleased interest evoked by diminutive scale and intricacy; the aspiration of tall slender verticals and the passivity and permanence of the horizontal line; the closed, static appearance of circular forms, and the dynamism of projecting, jagged shapes; the protection of the low cave-like space versus the freedom of the prairie; the strong feelings evoked by fundamental elements of the human shelter, such as the roof and the door, or of basic natural materials such as earth, rock, water, and plants. Spaces, knowingly shaped, will evoke an emotional response, and this response may be made appropriate to the function of the space.

There is a rich vocabulary of types of external space which can be drawn upon in developing the site plan: the vista, the court, the slot, the maze, the tunnel, the avenue or axis, the canopy, the free form, the hemicycle, the park, the bowl, the crest, the slope, the valley, the honeycomb, and many others. Most of these are part of the experience of everyone, but the designer takes up the habit of consciously examining them whenever he has the opportunity: checking real against apparent dimensions, making imaginary corrections, exploring the particular impact of the type. Such a storehouse of remembered spatial effects is part of his working equipment.

He may add to this storehouse an acquaintance with some typical and harmonious natural landscapes such as prairie, forest, meadow, dune, and marsh, or with those more particular and complex spaces which have become associated with certain human activities. These have developed historically as dominant site planning elements at various times and places. Such is the English residential square, with its town houses set about a small fenced park, and the urban Italian piazza, appearing suddenly among a web of narrow streets. Perhaps one thinks of a succession of interlinked college quadrangles, or of the formal French *place*, or of the cathedral close. Planted spaces may be managed as English parks, as formal gardens, or as groves. There is the winding, romantic suburban street, the broad avenue with its ranks of trees and grand perspective, the American parkway, the waterfront promenade, the arcade, the terrace. All of these are particularized kinds of space, which may be useful as type solutions in particular situations. They by no means exhaust the vast possibilities. Hopefully, new types of space will be developed in our culture, just as new building types are evolving. Such a development depends on conscious creative effort by many site designers.

David Crane

FIGURES 12, 13, and 14 *Three examples of traditional types of space: the Italian piazza (Venice), the French place (Nancy), the English square (Bath).*

Aerofilms Ltd.

Ground Form

In an urban area, the space may be defined by man-made structures; in less dense development, definition will be accomplished by the basic natural materials: earth, rock, water, and plant cover. In either case, the floor underfoot is the only continuous surface, and it plays a dominant role. The configuration of the floor is determined by the pre-existing topography, whose modelling must be thoroughly understood before work begins. Inspection will reveal certain key points in the shape of the land, such as the place where gradients change abruptly or from which commanding views may be had. The land may be divisible into small regions, each of homogeneous character, and with certain strategic linkages one to the other. Most sites will have a decided character, or pivotal features to which the plan can respond. These aspects pose problems for the designer and at the same time present him with special opportunities. Sites of strong topographic character will tend to dictate the basic organization of a plan, and to call for a simple, regular arrangement that will clarify the accidental terrain. Flat ground, or sites of more neutral character, will allow a much freer, more intricate patterning of buildings. These characteristics will become apparent, not only from the original reconnaissance, but gradually, as the design study goes forward and many alternatives are attempted.

An easy visual relation between man-made structures and topography is established when the long dimension of the structure, whether it be road or building, lies along the

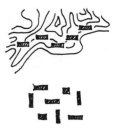

contour line. The building or road can be set low to the ground, and the natural contours are left as undisturbed as possible. This often proves to be the cheapest solution as well. At other times, the best solution (in terms of cost as well as esthetics) may be just the opposite: to allow the road or the axis of the building to plunge directly across the contours. This is a dramatic method which often clarifies the topographic structure in the strongest possible way. The most difficult relation occurs when the structural axes are diagonal to the contours. This solution is occasionally successful in skillful hands, but most often is liable to be awkward.

The designer must go beyond such local relationships if he wishes to clarify the basic structure of the land. He will arrange views and approaches so that the full scale of the hills and valleys may be appreciated and their character most sharply brought out. Sometimes this is best accomplished by "unnatural" designs, such as those which plant the hills and clear the valley bottoms to emphasize the drainage compartments, or which make a deep cut through a crest, so as to expose the earth or to make more dramatic the entrance into a valley. A town such as San Francisco, whose streets supposedly ignore the contours, is in fact very expressive of its dramatic site. The "natural" landscape pattern, with tall trees on the rich bottom land, and dwarf plants on the hills, actually tends to blur the sense of the underlying ground.

References 6 and 8

Buildings of uniform height, with their differentiated planes of roof and façade, may be arranged in step fashion on a hill, to give the sense of "piling up." Tall buildings may be placed on the heights, and low structures in the valleys. Long slabs may set back in echelon as they climb, or they may be stepped in vertical section. Special views may be opened up from the lowest to the highest points, and vice versa.

Inevitably, a new development changes the contours, often in a substantial way. These new ground shapes should fit harmoniously into the older landscape, or else be obvious artificial intrusions. If a harmonious fit is desired, transitions must be smoothly made, new land forms must be of the same family as the existing land forms, both in shape and scale; the whole should again make a consistent pattern. In humid temperate climates, for example, slopes are usually continuous and flowing, curve running into curve without intervening breaks, slopes meeting flat land with a concave profile.

Every landscape will have its own consistent family of land forms, due to the base material and its stratifications and angle of repose, the history of vulcanism or glaciation, the erosion cycle, the climate, and the vegetative cover.

At times, the ground form may be wilfully shaped to add interest, to mask unwanted features, to gain privacy, to increase apparent size, or to make the flow of roads and paths seem pleasant and easy. Slopes and level can be managed to give a calculated succession of views, allowing sequences of revealing and concealing, or affording sudden visual surprises. Paths and ground shapes can be manipulated

Martin Hürlimann

FIGURES 15 and 16 *The expression of site: the towering Potiala at Lhasa, and Frank Lloyd Wright's magical Taliesin East in Wisconsin.*

John Amarantides

FIGURE 17 *Use of a textured pavement in front of the Crown Zellerbach Building, San Francisco (Hertzka and Knowles, architects).*

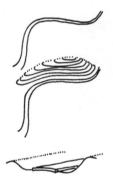

together, so that the movement of a road is psychologically explained, and affords a fine experience of movement in three dimension. An obtrusive road may be made to disappear by dropping it in a shallow but steep-sided cut.

Where the topography is monotonously level or shapeless, as it occasionally is, or where it must be radically disturbed for other reasons, then the designer may resort to a new and totally artificial topography. The whole problem of surface modelling shifts from the expression or modification of pre-existing structure to that of abstract sculpture on a vast scale, a sculpture which will unfold itself gradually to the observer as he passes through it. This has rarely been done for purely esthetic motives, but it is now technically possible. The creation of large-scale topography in imitation of natural form is quite difficult, however simple it may seem, and totally new topography is perhaps more safely confined to shapes which are obviously man-made.

These problems of topographic form are best studied in a model, even though the eventual decisions are more accurately conveyed to the contractor by a contour map. The work is sculptural; there is no substitute for pursuing it in a sculptural medium. Simple cardboard contour layer models may be used, which are cut and patched to show new dispositions. In a more complex modification of the ground, it may be best to use a plastic model material. The model will begin with the existing ground surface, and reshaping it without addition or subtraction of modelling material will indicate a solution in which cut and fill will roughly balance. Decisions on a scale model may later be transposed to more accurate drawings, or even directly to the field.

Ground Texture

The textural finish of the ground can be a source of delight in itself. It can also set general visual character and scale. It may be a harmonious background which unifies and sets off the whole scene, or it may be a dominant surface which reinforces the principal patterns and directions of the plan. The texture of the floor imparts sensations of touch as well as sight, and will direct and control activity on its surface. The details of activity that occur on the floor can in their turn be expressed to give textural pattern, and such differentiations play a useful role in guiding or controlling these activities: by distinguishing roads and footpaths, bicycle and car stalls, drainage runnels, play areas, or spots for standing and sitting.

Fine ground textures, such as moss, monolithic pavements, or close-cropped grass, tend to emphasize the shape and mass of the underlying round, and to increase its apparent size. They act as background for the objects that rise from, or are silhouetted against, them. Coarse textures, such as rough grass, cobble, bricks, or blocks, work in the opposite way, calling attention to the surface itself, rather than to the underlying mass or the objects above it. A centrally dished floor gives us a static sensation; a valley guides our vision along its course. Changes of level can act as space definers, or can be used to vary the point of view or to separate activity areas, as when raised beds protect planting from intensive traffic. Occasionally the surface may be left in rough and natural growth as a region for imaginative play.

Since the ground has such visual importance, we should consider its enrichment, not leave it to the casual attentions of the pavement or landscaping contractor. We tend to use a very scanty palette: little more than mown grass, bituminous macadam, or monolithic concrete. Their use is monotonous, sometimes ugly, and often quite unsuitable. Concrete is poor for running games; grass cannot bear the traffic in intensive areas. The range of surfacing available is in fact far wider, and it includes cultivated or stabilized earth; organic ground covers other than grass; overhead

Reference 38

Page 226

FIGURE 18 *Use of rock in Machu Picchu: expressive strength, rich texture.*

planting; tanbark; macadam; sand or gravel; asphalt or concrete with fillers, jointings, or surface aggregates; wood block or decking; terrazzos or mosaics; and pavements of blocks, bricks, tiles, or stones (cobbles, setts, or slabs). These materials may be used unbroken, or in patterned combinations.

Rock, Earth, and Water

Chinese stones from the Stone Catalogue of the Plain Garden (*17th century*)

Rock and earth are the primary site materials; they are our environmental base. Cuts and fills, pits and outcrops, cliffs, caves, and hills can communicate a sense of mass, a feeling of space, or an intuition of the planet whose surface we inhabit. Rock is an especially handsome material, although we tend to keep it well hidden with topsoil, or to prettify it in rock gardens. It is expressive of strength and permanence, of the working of powerful forces over long spans of time. It can be highly varied in form, color, grain, and surface texture, especially when weathered. Although often expensive, this material may be used to great effect in walls, paving, and steps, or as outcrops and isolated objects. Here again, in a scene intended to be continuous with some natural landscape, the manner in which rock is locally exposed must be observed and imitated: whether as ledge, talus, or scattered boulders.

Water is an equally elemental material, simple in nature, but extremely varied in its effects. The very variety of descriptive terms in the language is indicative of its potential richness in design: ocean, pool, sheet, jet, torrent, rill, drop, spray, cascade, film (plus an equal number of words for liquid motion: trickle, splash, foam, flood, pour, spurt, ripple, surge, run). The range of form, the changeableness and yet the unity, the intricate repetitive fluid movement, the suggestion of coolness and delight, the play of light and sound, as well as the intimate connection with life, all make water a superb material for outdoor use. It can evoke moods of gaiety, serenity, sorrow, mystery, majesty, contentment, or sheer voluptuousness. It is as attractive for play as it is for contemplation; it affects sound, smell, and touch as well as sight. Unfortunately, it entails problems of maintenance and safety as well: it may get dirty, breed insects or weeds, flood, or erode its banks.

Moving water gives a sense of life. Still water conveys a sense of unity and rest, and may be used to clarify a plan by indicating the base level. Usually it is wise to place still water at the lowest point in its immediate surroundings; certainly it must appear to lie naturally within the land form.

As a reflector, water may be used to play with light or it may act as a simple mirror. It can reflect the changing sky, in which case it should lie still and brimful in its container,

FIGURE 19 *A water pavement in the Miyajima Temple, Japan.*

with open borders. If the water is itself in shade, it may catch bright light. Or it may be set to reflect ground objects from certain viewpoints if the optics of reflection are kept in mind (the angle of reflection equals the angle of incidence), and if the water surface is not disturbed with plants or movement. If the water is shallow, a dark bottom surface will also improve its reflectivity.

The sound and movement of running water may be enhanced by the form of its container. Channels may be designed to throw water in the air, to strike it against obstacles, or to increase its turbulence. If the lip of a fall is undercut, all the volume will be visible; otherwise some of the water will flow invisibly and noiselessly down the rock face.

The edge of a water body is the principal focus of attention. A simply shaped water edge will convey clarity and stability; if it is complex and partly hidden, as along a wooded and irregular shore, it can evoke a sense of expectancy and extended space. This edge may be made abrupt and definite, or low, shelving, and obscure. In nature, these edges, whether as shores, islands, or stream margins, take on very characteristic forms due to waves, currents, and underlying geology. The alternation of undercut bank and gravel bar, for example, and the streamlined shape of islands and projections, is a characteristic of the meandering stream. If an apparently natural body of water is intended, these forms must be carefully observed.

Water is the center of interest in a landscape, whether near or distant. Perhaps we might reconsider our abandonment of the public fountain, our tendency to fill small ponds, and to put streams in culverts.

Plants

Next in importance is living plant material, trees, shrubs, and herbs, the material popularly associated with landscape work. Site planning is thought to be the spotting of trees and shrubs on a plan after houses and roads have been located. Site planning in our terms is the organization of a system of outdoor spaces, in which only one of the several materials that may be used is the plant cover. Many great landscapes are treeless, and there are handsome squares which do not include a plant of any description. To cover everything with trees, grass and vines is not an eternal principle of

Dimitra Katochianos

FIGURE 20 *A sparing use of vegetation may enhance its visual power. A street in the Cyclades, Greece.*

design. Even the best traditional use of grass, forest trees, and flower borders is ludicrous when imported into unsuitable climates.

Nevertheless, plants are one of the fundamental landscape materials, and if in public we worship the tree, in practice we often destroy it. Planting is often considered as an "extra" in site development, the first item to be cut when the budget pinches.

References 6 and 12

At the site planning scale, one is primarily concerned with groups of plants and with the general character of planted areas, rather than with individual specimens. Trees, large shrubs, and ground covers are the basic materials; their growth habits, form and texture are their most interesting features. The species available are first screened for those which are hardy for the given climate, microclimate, and soil condition. They must stand up to the wear of expected traffic, and demand no more care than can be furnished at the expected level of maintenance. These characteristics are detailed in Chapter 13 for some of the species which are especially useful for urban development in this climate.

Page 226

Even after screening there is a great range of effect available; colors, textures, and outlines can be played one against the other. The visible surface of the plant may have a texture that is fine or coarse, dull or shiny, close or open, stiff or trembling, clustered or even, smooth or modelled in depth. Its habit may be prostrate or upright, its shape rounded or angular, pyramidal or fastigiate, vasiform or tubular, or one of many other types. Forms will vary with season, and between youth and maturity. Each species has its own pattern, its own peculiar way in which leaves, buds, and stems arrange themselves, a pattern only distorted in the individual by the accidents of age and exposure.

Species can be sited to make a general effect or to contrast among themselves. Plants of similar form but dramatically different texture may be juxtaposed, or shapes may be contrasted: an angular, dynamic tree beside a rounded, static shrub, or an arrangement of upright, recumbent, and prostrate forms. A delicate fern may bring out the character of a massive rock. Since it is easier to predict the texture of a plant than its particular form, and since that texture does not vary from different points of view as much as does the individual shape, it is usually advisable when working at the site planning scale to dispose plants primarily according to their textures, and according to ideas of general massing.

The choice of plants will be influenced by their visual fit with the setting: the relation of their shapes to those of buildings and of the ground, the apparent harmony with the climate and with native vegetation. As has been noted above, they may be used to clarify the shape of the ground. Alternatively, where topography or man-made structure has an awkward form, then plants may be used to mask or subdue those faults, whether by covering or shading them, by the blurring of outlines or the redirecting of attention.

It is usually desirable to concentrate a number of specimens of one species in order to give the effect of that type. Even in mixed groups, only two or three species are used, and these are not intermixed evenly but located in clusters which thin out into clusters of another type. But it is unwise to plant a single kind of plant everywhere, since a fatal disease may strike that species, as it has the chestnut and the elm.

Trees should be considered as they will appear in three dimensions, to their true height and size, and not as abstract circles on the plan. The appearance of the arrangement must be imagined at the beginning as well as at maturity, in winter as well as in summer. At planting, they should be set far enough apart from each other and from structures to prevent interference and distortion of shape, unless such a distorted shape, of the effect of a solid mass of planting, is desired. Large forest trees, for example, if meant to come to full shape, must be 50 to 60 feet apart, and 20 feet from buildings. Trees take time to come to maturity: final effects may not take place for thirty or even fifty years, and what seems to be pleasant siting in the beginning may later mean desperate over-crowding.

This problem of maturity is a perennial one in the landscaping of building developments. New sites are typically barren, and old ones overgrown. To some extent this can be avoided by the careful preservation of existing trees, but in dense development this is usually possible only for avenues or clumps in strategic locations, or for occasional fine specimens. The ground surface is usually disturbed too much for any general retention of existing cover.

Mature trees will not survive a violent change of habitat. The ground may not be cut away near their roots, nor may more than a few inches be added to the grade, although a large well, with radial drains and 6 inches of crushed stone out to the drip of the branches, may sometimes save the plant. Trees which grew in a wood must be preserved in a clump, since they have shallow roots, while trees that were originally isolated or in open fence lines should be kept so. The preservation of large but decayed or ancient trees, which are past the prime for that species, is also questionable, since their removal after development is complete will be more difficult. But whether tactics of preservation or of replanting are used, landscaping is not done once and then forgotten. An area should be growing successive generations of trees, according to a regular program.

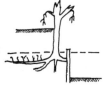

For immediate effect, mature specimens, even trees thirty feet in height, may be put in place. This is an expensive and demanding technique, usually reserved for key places. Another solution is to use succession planting, in which quick-growing and slow-growing species are planted together, the rapid plants then being cut out as the others mature. Or plants may initially be put in at close spacings, being thinned out as they approach maturity. Both of these techniques require effective maintenance, stern enough to continue cutting out despite the protests of tree-lovers.

If land can be held in reserve at a large enough scale, it might be possible to plant lines and masses of trees in a pattern suitable for future development. The initial investment would be small, while the development when it occurred would benefit from a mature planted setting. Where this has happened accidentally, as in the resumption of development in an abandoned subdivision, the effect has often been quite handsome.

In any case, planting is not a frill to be left up to the future occupant. Trees, ground cover, hedges, and shrubs, the main framework of the planting, should be built in before occupancy. Neither is landscaping a camouflage or green stuffing to be packed between buildings, nor should it be designed as a series of small isolated settings for individual structures. It must be conceived as a total pattern, continuous throughout the site. Lines of tall trees, visible from a distance, may mark major axes in the plan, clumps of special texture may make focal points, masses may define major spaces, homogeneous styles of planting may mark off important areas.

It has been customary in housing developments to consider only the planting of public areas, streets, and parks, leaving private lots to be planted at will. Along the streets, moreover, we have used a single solution with monotonous regularity: the double line of street trees. While the planted avenue can be handsome, particularly when it is broad, set with high arching trees, and leads to some important destination, it is not the only available style of landscaping. The avenue of trees may in fact be all the more dramatic if confined to certain major ways. Minor streets can be planted as spatial compartments, or with occasional tree masses or specimens, or in other ways. Small trees may often be in better scale with narrow streets or low structures. The designer need not confine himself to the street alone, nor to a single solution on that street.

Detail

Reference 38

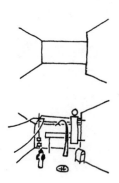

Within the spatial framework, and in addition to the primary materials of buildings, earth, rock, water, and plants, the site plan includes many details. Their number becomes apparent when we try to catalogue the furniture of some existing area: fences, seats, signal boxes, utility poles, light poles, meters, trash cans, fireplugs, manholes, wires, lights, and so on. This "near world" of detail may be as important for the appearance of the whole as is the basic spatial structure. This can be particularly true for the regular user of an area. Color, form, and texture may be used to focus attention or divert it, to provide harmony or contrast. The texture of the floor, the shape of the curbs or the steps, the

Leon Lewandowski

FIGURE 21 *How the street details will be used is what counts.*

design of street furniture, are the things close to the person that present themselves directly and immediately to the eye. But if these things are to be finely shaped, they require a substantial investment of time for design and supervision.

Design and placement of these details is normally left to hazard, as if an architect were to be indifferent to the location and style of the fittings with which his building was equipped. Such indifference may be possible where a long tradition of design controls the shape of details, but it can be fatal when the technology is evolving rapidly. Therefore the designer must consider where the wires will go or what shape the fireplugs will have. He can simply insure harmony, or he can go further and consider how the landscape details are used. This will bring him to the placement of telephones, alarms, and mail boxes so that they are quickly found; it will make him think about the route over which the trash can must be moved; or it may influence him to provide frequent seats along the public way.

In time, we may come to the point where we are moved, not simply to harmonize or conceal, but rather to declare these important technical functions openly. Instead of seeking to hide the power lines, we may find ways of making

Walker Evans

them handsome and expressive, in the manner that long-distance high-voltage lines have already achieved. It might simply be confusing to make all the technical apparatus of a site immediately apparent to the eye, but we may find handsome ways of expressing them clearly as a group, or of emphasizing the legibility of selected elements.

Fences and walls are of particular importance in the site plan, both functionally, as they delimit areas and confer privacy, and visually, as they form spaces and provide vertical texture. Fencing should be an integral part of the site plan, provided from the beginning to accomplish visual and functional objectives. Too often fences are left to be added haphazardly. Or, if installed, they will tend to come to a single ugly solution: the chain link fence. This recent product can be compared only to barbed wire in its appearance and emotional meaning.

There are many fine fencing materials. Wooden rails, pickets, stakes or lattice, wooden boards or sheets, woven saplings or reeds, stretched or woven wire, iron rails, plastics, canvas, woody plants (see Chapter 13), brick, stone, earth, poured concrete or concrete block are all amenable to inventive use. Numerous patterns are part of our own historical tradition: picket fences, rail fences, serpentine brick walls, or high hedges; and their symbolic connotations are strong. Gardens throughout the world, Japanese gardens in particular, are rich sources of fence patterns, and many new forms are being invented today by American garden designers.

Another kind of site detail merits separate discussion: the signs which have become such a dominant, and generally such an ugly and chaotic, part of our landscape. Again the effort of most designers has been to suppress or control them, as something intrinsically bad. Yet they are necessary to explain and direct activity, and at times turn out to be very dramatic features.

For hedges, see page 227

A landscape must communicate to its users, whether by conventional signs, or by the observer's knowledge of the meaning of visible shapes and motions. In an increasingly complex world, the messages carried by a landscape must increasingly be embodied in abstract symbolic devices. They are ugly and chaotic, not by nature, but because they are thoughtlessly used, ambiguous, redundant, and fiercely competitive. Rather than suppressing these messages, it should be the designer's aim to guide and control them so that they can become even more expressive: preventing destructive competition, promoting contrast and rhythm, giving the signs a basic continuity, using form and color symbolically.

More signs and symbols might be employed to explain the meaning of various parts of the landscape and to orient the observer within it. One criterion of a landscape is that it be meaningful as well as well-ordered. To the maximum extent possible, its parts should be expressive of their position, their function, or of the human values attached to them. Such meaningfulness arises almost automatically in a settled landscape which has long been occupied by the same group, engaged in the same activities, and seized by the same values and aspirations. In a newer and more mobile situation, the consciously devised abstract symbol may be of significant value. Many existing signs are used in this way, although with poor efficiency. The principal objective should be to enhance their power, and to remove those which are extraneous to the scene, as for example the advertisements of products produced and consumed elsewhere.

Viewpoint and Sequence

A landscape is typically seen from a rather limited set of viewpoints. These are especially the paths along which the observer moves — and along which the forward view is sharply distinguished from the backward view — and certain key stationary views, as from windows and principal entrances. The lines of sight from these critical fixed or moving points should be analyzed carefully. This may be done by quick perspective studies, or by traces of the cone of vision on plan and section. Even better, the design may be studied in model form, placing the eye close to the ground level of the model at the strategic points of view. Various devices may be used to increase the sense of reality: pinhole viewers, mirrors, or periscopes, which project the observer into any part of the model and allow him to see it as though he were walking through it.

However analyzed, the sight lines may be manipulated by slight shifts in ground level or in the position of opaque elements to produce strong effects of masking, foreshortening, or altered form. The eye may be directed by framing the view or by its tendency to travel along a valley or perpendicular to slopes. It may be drawn along a confined channel or a rank of repeated forms to rest on the sky or on a raised or silhouetted terminal feature. It may be attracted to some focal object, thus in effect masking out surrounding

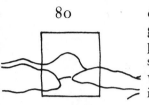

Figure 23, page 82

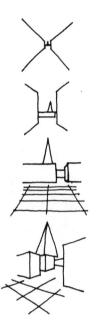

detail. A distant view is usually enhanced by some foreground object to which it may be contrasted; it is often improved when framed or subdivided by nearby planting or structure so that attention is concentrated. Thus the total view may be organized into parts, or perhaps only a hint of its full sweep may be given.

Since the landscape is usually experienced by a moving observer, it is not the single view that is important so much as the cumulative effect of a sequence of views. A lack of formal balance at any one moment may be of much less consequence than, for example, the sensation of release produced when the observer comes out from a narrow slot into a broad expanse. This is the radical difference between landscape and pictorial composition, and serves to explain why it may be virtually impossible to take good photographs of some fine environments.

Most important, therefore, is a sequential analysis of the series of views, or the connected chain of spaces. For example, a major view may at first only be hinted at, be succeeded by a more intimate view of something else, be repeated but with a dominant foreground, disappear in a closely confined space, and finally reappear in its full sweep. The sensations encountered along the principal approach to a development would be of particular concern. The expected direction and speed of the observer are critical, since sight becomes restricted to a narrower forward quadrant as speed increases, and since spatial effects pleasant at a walking pace may be imperceptible at sixty miles an hour, and vice versa. Each type of motion has an appropriate scale of spatial treatment.

Questions of orientation become significant: the apparent direction toward a goal, the marking of the distance traversed, the clarity of entrance and exit, the explanation to the moving observer of the basic structure and his place in it. An apparent succession of arrivals, like the series of runs and landings on a stair, may be more pleasant than a single protracted approach. Each event should in some way prepare for and anticipate the next one, without completely foretelling it, so that the observer receives them as an ever fresh but coherent development. Similarly, the environment should have a form which is readily apparent to the distant or hasty glance, and yet reveals new features and organizations when inspected more closely. The form of the motion itself has esthetic meaning: it may be direct or indirect, fluid or formal, smooth or erratic, delicate or brutal, divergent or convergent, purposeful or whimsical, up or down.

FIGURE 22 *Each event should anticipate the next: entrance to the Piazza Grande, Arezzo.*

Paul Spreiregen

In such a landscape potential motion takes on importance as well: a road suggests direction, and the eye follows it as a thread that links the whole together. Broad flat steps will seem easy and inviting, and those that are narrow, steep, and curving will appear dramatic and exciting, seeming to lead to some hidden promise. This effect of potential motion is greatly strengthened by objects visibly in progressive movement: ships, trains, cars, walkers.

The essential visual criterion of a site design is that it should exhibit a rhythmical continuity: a coherent succession of spaces or textures or objects in which each part relates harmoniously to the next but which makes a constant play of variation on the basic theme. If there is a chain of spaces, they should seem to be part of one extended whole, even while alternating from open to close, from simple to intricate, from brilliant to subdued. Thus an early step in the site planning process is to develop the basic spatial form and to analyze its visual consequences when seen as a sequence. It is often useful to outline or shade the space between opaque objects, emphasizing this primary visual sensation. The spaces should be considered as a total pattern — not seen flatwise from the air, but as a progression through which one moves.

1

2

3

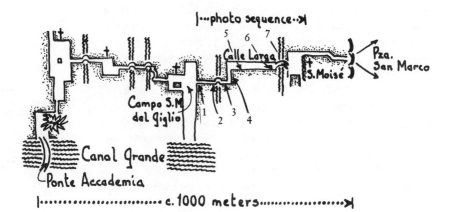

FIGURE 23 *An episode in the walk from the Accademia Bridge to the Piazza San Marco, Venice: a dramatic sequence of space, activity, and texture.*

Visual Structure

Perception of the environment is a process of creating a visual hypothesis, the building of an organized mental image which is based on the experience and purposes of the observer, as well as on the stimuli which reach his eye. In building his visual organization, he will seize on congenial physical characteristics: continuity and closure of form; differentiation, dominance, or contrast of a figure on a ground; symmetry, order, repetition, or simplicity of form. Thus there are techniques by which structure and relatedness can be developed in areas too extensive to be seen at one glance. Rhythmic repetitions may be used, such as the appearance of open spaces or dominant masses at regular intervals. Parts may be related by maintaining a common scale of space or mass, or simply by similarities of form, material, color or detail, such as common building materials, a homogeneous ground surface, or uniform planting. The parts may reveal a common single-minded purpose or the impact of a dominant force, such as a powerful climate or a highly organized culture. In a more subtle way, features of one part may recall those of another without directly imitating them, as when fountains may recall the sea.

Sharp variations are also a way of relating parts if there is some continuity of access, form, or character between those parts, and if one of the contrasting parts is clearly dominant. Thus a dark and narrow street is related to the broad avenue on which it debouches, and a quiet park is tied to the intensive shopping which fronts on it. Related contrasts, seen in sequence or at one glance, bring out the essence of a feature, and put us in touch with a wide range of experience. Near may be compared with far, fluid with fixed, familiar with strange, light with dark, solid with empty, ancient with new.

Continuity depends on the important transitions, the joints between house and ground and between house and house, corners, gateways between spaces, or the upper edge of objects at the skyline. These points of transition are often the most noticeable features at the outdoor scale. They must be articulate if the spaces are to be readable and if they are to seem coherently joined. The classic architectural emphasis on cornices, base courses, and door moldings can be echoed in the roof silhouettes, terraces, and spatial entrances of the site plan.

As a consequence of the great number of objects in the exterior scene, both grouping and contrast must be used so as to bring the complex under perceptual control. Clusters of structures may be set off by open space, or a large space may be surrounded by dense occupancy. Houses of similar kind will be grouped in visual units, or trees of one species planted together, to give the sense of "street" or "birchwood" rather than "house" or "birch tree." Parts may be interrelated by referring them all to the same dominant, as to a church steeple or a central space.

So complex and loose is the whole that the effect to be sought is usually broad and simple rather than precise and intricate. Richness is inherent in the material and an intricate plan may end in confusion. Not only is the material complex in itself, but it is often in motion, seen in different lights and at different stages of growth. The scene must be able to accept all this without losing its basic form. This does not necessarily require the simplicity of formal geometry, but only that breadth of treatment which is in consonance with the scale at which the work is being done. A good site plan is basically straightforward and, while being highly refined at certain critical points, is often almost coarse in its over-all form.

The main structure of a site design is most often created by the use of some sort of hierarchy, dominance, or centrality. Thus there may be a central space to which all other spaces are subordinate and related, or a dominant path which links many minor paths together. Similarly, in regard to sequence, it is customary to organize a principal approach, having a gateway or point of beginning, and developing to a climactic point of arrival, where there is a strong sense of place and of being at the heart of things. These are tested structural methods, and they underlie most of the successful site designs of the past.

But these are not the only possible structural types, especially in large, complex, or changing sites. Many-centered forms might be used, or interlinking networks of paths, or continuously varying characteristics of activity and space, or multiple sequences which have no determinate beginning or end. Since these forms are complex and largely untested, they are the more difficult to employ without a lapse into disorder. Moreover, they still rely on variations sequentially organized, on emphasis, and on grouping.

This formal visual structure cannot lead an independent existence, but must be congruent with the actual use of the site. Visual climaxes must correspond with the most intensive or meaningful activity locations; the principal visual sequences should mesh with the most important lines of circulation. We may generalize by saying that the basic aspects of site organization — activity location, circulation, and visual form — should function together in detail and also have a formal structure that is mutually congruent.

Spaces and facilities not only require proportioning of their parts and scaling to the human observer, but also they must be sized to the expected intensity of activity. For example, a square of certain dimensions may in a central location seem cramped and oppressive because of the crowds of people using it, while at the periphery where the pedestrians are few, it would appear empty, vast, and lonely. A footpath passing through back lots may seem excessively long and uninviting, while a path of the same dimensions and form, but bordered by various activities and located to offer a convenient path for many people, will appear important, exciting, and relatively brief.

This problem of interrelation is further complicated by the necessity of coordinating the design of individual structures with that of the site plan as a whole. These structures have a pattern of use, circulation, and visual form that should mesh with the corresponding patterns of the site plan. The internal circulation of the building is an extension of the external site circulation. Interior architectural space is part of the total site space. Visual sequences begin in the hallways of houses; views from windows are significant; building shapes are fundamental elements of the external spatial form. Building and site must flow together. This does not require that all walls be glass and that rocks and trees invade the rooms, but only that inside form fit into outside form, and that a harmonious joint be made between man-made structure and the land. The relation of floor level to ground level and the character of the openings in the building envelope are of especial importance here. For this reason, architectural and site design are ideally done simultaneously, whether by a single individual or a cooperating team. The special cases where site design must be separated from structure design, and the special problems that they entail, are discussed in Chapter 7.

Reference 23

Page 103

The designer is constrained to use a strategy of concentration. In achieving his visual effects he is always confronted by a shortage of resources, whether it be of money, of public open space, of structure, of movement, or of concentrated activity. Rather than attempting to use every kind of element and every type of structure, spread out over the entire area, he concentrates his resources: conserves his views and displays them at their best, brings things together at focal points and along main lines, economizes here to afford some luxury there, avoids open spaces or pedestrian ways which are beyond his power to equip or maintain. One of his crucial decisions is how much area or activity or visual experience he is able to dominate and organize. Can he control a large landscape by means of axes and dispersed elements, or must he be content to structure one strategic point?

In a site plan, therefore, we are dealing with the total organization of space, a space which is loose, continuous and dynamic in nature. This space is formed with buildings, earth, rock, water, plants, and light. The criteria for visual success are first, that this space be imageable, i.e., well structured and vivid in form, endowed with a pervading sense of place. Second, it must be conceived as a sequential experience, rhythmically organized, with contrast and variety, yet with strong continuity. Third, it must be meaningful: highly expressive of the nature, function, and value of the place and the uses that occupy it.

Chapter 6

Light, Noise, and Air

We are immersed in an ocean of air, constantly subject to its variations of temperature, humidity, and purity, and to the light and sound that is being propagated through it. Swimming in this ocean, we have strong preferences for certain ranges or rhythms of light and noise intensity, of air purity and effective temperature. Natural climates are erratic and violent, and there are man-made intrusions of noise and airborne impurities. Men defend themselves by physiological adaptations, and by the use of clothing and structure. But it is also possible to manipulate the climate by the arrangement and choice of site.

The general climate of any region sets the stage. It is expressed in data on variations in temperature, humidity, precipitation, cloudiness, speed and prevailing direction of winds, and the sun path for that latitude. These are the outside constraints within which the site planner operates, and he must have them before him in some concise form. Such data is available for most areas of the world, but will have to be evaluated for site planning purposes. The essential questions are most likely to be: What is the duration and intensity of precipitation that must be warded off and drained away? What are the favorable and unfavorable winds, and from what direction do they come? At what time of day or season should direct sun radiation be avoided or invited, and from what direction is it coming? When and in what way does the effective temperature move outside the comfort zone? Standard data is likely to include temperature and humidity ranges, wind direction and force, occurrence and intensity of rain or snow, sun directions and the hours of sunshine. Although simplified data is wanted, average data will not suffice. It is the extreme conditions that are uncomfortable, and therefore ranges and average maximums and minimums are likely to be most useful.

Page 219

The effective temperature is a sensation produced by the combined effect of radiation and ambient temperature, relative humidity, and air movement. The comfort zone may be roughly defined as follows: most people in the temperate zone, sitting indoors in the shade in light clothing, will feel tolerably comfortable at temperature ranges between 70° and 80°F as long as the relative humidity lies between 20 percent and 50 percent. As humidity increases, these same people will begin to be uncomfortable at lower and lower temperatures, until the relative humidity reaches about 75 percent, when general discomfort at any temperature sets in. But if they are sitting in a draft, the range of tolerable temperature shifts upward, so that temperatures of 85° may be quite comfortable in the 20 to 50 percent humidity range, if local air is moving at 200 feet per minute. Indoor air moving more slowly than 50 feet per minute is generally unnoticed, while flows of 50 to 100 feet per minute are pleasant and hardly noticed. Breezes from 100 to 200 are pleasant but one is constantly aware of them, while those from 200 to 300 are first slightly, and then annoyingly, drafty.

The designer will do what he can to see that indoor and even outdoor effective temperatures lie within this comfort zone. Depending on the general climate, he will induce or check the flow of air, let in or block the sun, humidify or dry the air, raise or lower the temperature. Outdoors the site planner is somewhat more concerned with summer climates, since in winter clothing can be used for protection, and less time is spent outdoors. Yet in the cold seasons a great deal can be done to moderate the severity of climate or to prolong the season of outdoor activity by the use of wind shields, radiation traps, or even outdoor heating.

When the designer works in a region new to him, a study of the traditional buildings of the locality and of their climatic advantages and defects will be of special value. He is particularly interested in the study of the microclimate, that local modification of the general climate which is imposed by the special shape of a small area: its topography,

References 40 and 44

cover, ground surface, and man-made forms. The micro-climatic effects give him clues for changing the general climate in a favorable way.

These effects are typically very local ones, since the microclimate often changes within distances of a few feet or less. As a significant phenomenon, it is confined to a shallow zone close to the skin of the earth, no more than a few stories high. It is a product of the movement and interchange of heat, water vapor, air impurities, and light and sound energy, as this interchange is influenced by the different surfaces and media it encounters. The heat balance is the fundamental phenomenon, that constant interchange between sun, earth, and atmosphere, producing small climates which fluctuate markedly on a daily or seasonal cycle, particularly at the interface between earth and air.

Albedo, Conductivity, and Air Movement

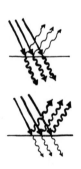

Heat is exchanged by radiation, conduction, and convection. There are three corresponding characteristics of the media to be considered: albedo, conductivity, and the nature of air movement. Albedo is a characteristic of surfaces, being the percent of the total radiant energy of a given wavelength incident on a surface which is reflected back by that surface instead of being absorbed. A surface with an albedo of 1.0 is a perfect mirror, reflecting back everything that shines on it, without darkening the reflected image or receiving any heat itself. A surface whose albedo is zero is a perfect matte surface, reflecting nothing and soaking up all the heat radiated upon it. These same properties also appear when the flow of radiation reverses: a hot surface of high albedo radiates its heat outwards only slowly, while a hot surface of low albedo radiates quickly as well as receiving quickly. Albedo may therefore be imagined as the relative permeability of a surface to radiant energy flowing in either direction: high albedo surfaces are resistant to this flow and low albedo surfaces are permissive. In the same way, surfaces may also be relatively absorbent or relatively reflective to the sound waves falling on them, although the albedo of a surface with respect to radiant energy bears no relation to its "albedo" with respect to sound.

Albedos of natural surfaces vary markedly for radiation within the visible spectrum:

fresh snow	0.80–0.85
cloud surfaces	0.60–0.90
old snow	0.42–0.70
fields, meadow	
tillage	0.15–0.30
sand and heath	0.10–0.25
forest	0.05–0.18
surface of the sea	0.08–0.10

For the visible spectrum, the albedo of wet or dark-colored surfaces tend to be lower than those of dry or light-colored surfaces. But the albedo of a surface may be quite different for different wavelengths: for infrared radiation the albedo of most natural materials is rather low.

Conductivity refers to the speed with which heat, or sound, passes through a given material, once having penetrated its surface. Heat flows rapidly through substances of high conductivity, and vice versa. Variation in conductivity is the basis of insulation, and also controls the rate with which reservoirs of heat in the earth or the sea can be built up or released. Commercial insulation, for example, is a material of very low conductivity, thermal or acoustic. A piece of warm metal feels much hotter than wood of the same temperature, simply because the metal, with its high conductivity, releases its heat more rapidly. The conductivity of natural materials in general decreases as these materials are drier, less dense, and more porous. For example, the thermal conductivity of some natural materials decreases in the following order: solid granite, ice, wet sand, humus, wet marshy soil, still water, old snow, dry sand, fresh snow, peat, still air.

Heat and sound are also distributed by fluid movement, or convection. The significant factors here are speed and turbulence, or the degree to which movement occurs as random eddies rather than as a steady directed flow. Turbulence disperses heat, or sound waves, or impurities, while steady flow may contain them and thus preserve contrasts. Air turbulence may increase with height, at the microclimatic scale, and then decrease again in the upper levels of air. Wind directions can be strikingly different at different levels, while its speed tends to increase with height because of the surface friction of the ground: the wind speed 3 inches off the ground may be 30 percent, the speed 6 inches up 50 percent, and that 3 feet up 80 percent, of the wind speed 6 feet above the ground. Wind speed in itself, by its rate of transport of heat, has a marked effect on cooling. A 30-miles-per-hour wind with air at 30°F has six times the cooling effect of still air at 10°F. Any frostbitten nose will give testimony to this. As another example, when a 12-miles-per-hour wind at 32°F is reduced in speed to 3 miles per hour before it strikes a house, fuel consumption in that house may be halved.

Lastly, we must consider the ability of an object to store the heat it receives, an ability which results from its total mass and its specific heat, or the amount of heat energy absorbed by a unit mass for each unit rise in temperature. A cool object of high specific heat and large mass, whose interior is accessible to heat flow via conduction or convection, will absorb large amounts of heat over long periods. When exterior temperatures drop, it can also return that energy over a long interval. A house with thick masonry walls will be cooler in the heat of day and warmer at night than a more flimsy structure. Large water bodies, with their internal convection and low albedo, act like climatic flywheels to even out the daily or seasonal swings of temperature.

Surface Material

Of first importance is the nature of surface materials. If the ground has a low albedo and a high conductivity, then the resulting microclimate is mild and stable, since excess heat is quickly absorbed and stored, and as quickly released when general temperatures drop. Surface materials of high albedo and low conductivity, on the other hand, make for a microclimate of extremes, since they do not help to balance the swings of the weather. Thus the sea, or grass, or wet ground tend to even out the climate, while the weather over snow or pavement is more violent: hot in the sun and cold at night. The monthly range of temperature in June in one locality, when the air temperature varied by only 45°F, was 106° on a bituminous pavement, and 52° in the grass. On a day when the standard temperature was 77°, the surface of a concrete walk was at 95°, and that of a dark slate roof at 110°.

Drainage of wet land increases the albedo and decreases conductivity, and so makes the local climate more unstable. At the same time, humidity will fall, and the cooling effect of evaporation from damp ground will be lost. A water surface usually has a low albedo, but not for light striking it at a low angle of incidence. Here the albedo increases rapidly and the water acts as a mirror. Heat and light are directed at waterside objects both from the air and from the water surface. This may be unpleasant in a summer house facing the late afternoon sun across a lake, or desirable for the growth of crops on steep slopes overlooking water to the east or west.

A high density of man-made structures or a substantial area of paving increases the albedo significantly and thus makes for higher summer temperatures. And since the land drains more quickly and is more impervious to water vapor, the general humidity tends to fall. A deep fall of fresh snow will raise daytime temperatures by reflection while insulating the surfaces it covers.

Slope

The slope of ground surfaces has an effect as important as that of surface material. The word climate is in fact derived from the Greek for "slope." The principal factors are the orientation of ground with respect to the sun, and the general form of topography as it affects air movement.

Orientation is most critical in the middle latitudes, since in the far north much of the radiation is diffuse, coming from a cloudy sky and illuminating north slopes as much as south slopes. In the tropics, the high angle of the sun tends to minimize the differences between the orientation of slope. Maximum direct radiation is received by the surface which is perpendicular to the direction of the sun, and this depends on latitude, season, and hour of the day. Thus a south slope will receive more sun than flat land, and, in midsummer, a northwest wall may even be warmer than a south wall. A 10 percent slope to the south will receive as much direct radiation (and to that extent have the same climate) as flat land 6 degrees closer to the equator, or the difference in latitude between New York City and Memphis, Tennessee. On a cloudless day at 40° N. latitude, the total direct and diffuse radiation on a 10 degree (17½ percent) slope attains the following approximate percentages of the possible maximum, depending on season and the orientation of the slope:

Data on sun direction is given on page 222

Slope Direction	Midsummer	Equinox	Midwinter
North	95%	55%	15%
East or West	100	60	25
South	100	70	35

The same data for a perpendicular wall, (where the possible maximum is about one-half of that in the first table, is:

Wall faces	Midsummer	Equinox	Midwinter
North	40%	15%	5%
East or West	90	70	25
South	50	95	100

Structures will receive substantially different amounts of radiation depending on their orientation. In the higher latitudes most of the rooms of a dwelling should get some sun on a winter day, and all of them should receive adequate daylight. One will not face rooms with large glass areas toward the low western sun of summer, which is difficult to shield off. But, except for such simple rules, it is useless to set down any general precepts for building orientation. There are many techniques of sunshielding, much radiation is diffuse and directionless, and variety of outlook is also desirable. Windows to the north may look upon a landscape flooded with sun, especially where living units face outward in more than one direction from a building. Particularly when dealing with tall structures, one may be just as concerned with how their orientation and placement affect the radiation falling on the ground about their base. Artificial warming and cooling is far more difficult to achieve outdoors than in. Instead of relying on standard orientations, a whole system of measures must be taken to produce an optimum local climate.

The general form of the topography also affects air movement. Wind speeds on the crest of a ridge may be 20 percent greater than those on the flat, while wind is generally quieter on the lee side than on the weather side of a hill. But this latter condition may be reversed if the lee slope is gentle, and the weather side is steep.

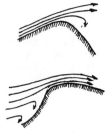

See below

Cold air floods are a nocturnal phenomenon on open slopes. A layer of air near the ground is cooled by the ground beneath it, which is losing its heat by radiation outward to the night sky. This film of cold air flows downhill as a shallow sheet, gathering into a stream in open valleys, or a still pool where blocked by some "dam" of topography or cover. Positions at the foot of long open slopes are notoriously cold and damp, and hollows become frost pockets. Such floods can be diverted by barriers uphill, or prevented from pooling by breaching the downhill dam.

Cold air pockets may persist over the next day if they are large enough, and especially if fog or haze has formed to prevent the sun from warming the ground surface. Now the air is coldest close to the ground, and warmer higher up, a situation called an "inversion" because it is the reverse of the normal daytime condition. The formation is stable because cold air is heavier than warm, and there is none of the customary upward movement of warm, light surface air.

If the day should also be windless, then fog and smoke will not be dissipated, and thus smog will collect over urban areas.

Other local air movements may be set up by topography, such as the shore breeze. At the shore of seas or very large lakes on an otherwise windless day there will typically be an afternoon breeze blowing from the sea, and a night breeze off the land. This is due to the warm air rising now from land and now from the water, depending on the relative warmth of each. The resulting inflow of surface air at the bottom of the rising column creates the surface breeze.

In brief, in the temperate zone, the best local climates tend to be on south or southeast slopes, and near water, and on upper or middle slopes rather than at their foot or crest.

Plants and Structures

All these effects are in their turn modified by the plant cover or the structures which occur on the land. Plants alter the form of the surface, increasing the area for radiation and transpiration, shading the ground, braking air movement, and trapping air within the stand. The net result is a cooler, more humid, more stable microclimate. Plants will also trap a certain amount of smoke and dust, which is more likely to affect their own health than it is to purify the air in any substantial way. Thick belts of shrubs or trees are effective windbreaks. They reduce wind velocities by more than 50 percent for a distance downwind of ten times their height.

Structures, like plants, will also affect air movement. They will block and divert winds, or may channel them along narrow openings. This may be desirable along a street in summer, or may be quite disagreeable underneath a large slab building on stilts in a winter storm. Warm weather wind should be accepted and winter wind be diverted. Both effects may be achieved if the prevailing wind direction shifts with the seasons, as it often does. However, we need not make the mistake of early authors such as Vitruvius: winds do not always blow from standardized prevailing directions!

Unfortunately, we still have a great deal to learn about wind movements within groups of buildings, and very little can be said about them. In general, the taller and the longer a building or other barrier to the wind, the more extensive is the eddy on the downwind side, a zone of low pressure

where air is relatively quiet and is moving erratically or even in a contrary direction to prevailing flow. But the thicker such a building becomes in the direction of air flow, the smaller the area of wind eddy, to a limited extent. Thus a thin, tall, long wall is the most effective windbreak. Surprisingly enough, it may be more effective if it is not completely impenetrable to the wind, so that pressure is not lowered so far that it causes strong air turbulence.

So complex is air movement between groups of buildings that it may be desirable, for example, to bring a low building close up behind a tall building in order to improve the ventilation of the lower structure! Therefore it is useful to study air movements through the site on a scale model. Such studies are best made with technical apparatus, by trained personnel, in a low-speed wind tunnel; this is the only way to obtain quantitative data on probable wind speed and pressure. Without such apparatus, however, it is still possible to predict the general pattern of wind movement, including wind direction, the rough relative intensities of flow, and the regions of calm or of gustiness. This can be done in the simple device described in Chapter 13.

Page 224

The course of winds affects the rate of cooling, the removal of impurities, the transmission of sound, and even such details as the play of fountains. Turbulent air disperses sound waves, steady winds affect their audible reach. If winds are wanted in order to lower the effective temperature, remember that air flows more than six feet off the ground are of little avail. Local cover and structure has most effect when general winds are light and steady. With strong wind and much turbulence, their influence is more erratic. Under such conditions, for example, smoke contamination will disperse rapidly, even downwind from the source, and regardless of local cover.

Shading

Structures and trees also modify the climate in their shadow by blocking direct sun radiation. The designer wishes to arrange these shadows to avoid radiation when it is hot and to receive it when it is cold. Deciduous trees are ideal, since they cut off the summer sun and let the winter sun shine through. In other cases, the site planner wishes to provide a variety of sun and shade at any moment, so that the inhabitants may choose their own preferred climate. To study the whole system of moving shadows, the planner must

Alimari Photo

FIGURE 24 *Microclimate: the shade defines the crowd on a hot summer day (Via Calzaiuoli, Florence).*

understand the geometry of the sun path in the heavens, and how it varies with hour, date, and latitude.

At the vernal and autumnal equinox, the sun appears to rise due east at 6 A.M., rising and falling in an arc which at local noon is at its highest point. At this time, in the northern hemisphere, the sun appears due south of the observer, and its angular height above the southern horizon equals ninety degrees less the latitude of the place. In midwinter, the day is shorter, the sun rises and sets well to the south of the equinoctial points, and its noon position is 23½ degrees below equinoctial noon. In midsummer, the day is longer, rising and setting are well to north of east or west, and the sun at noon is 23½ degrees above equinoctial noon. In 40-degree latitudes, the midwinter rising is about 30 degrees south of east and an hour and a half later, and the setting 30 degrees south of west and an hour and a half earlier, than they are at the equinox, while at midsummer just the opposite occurs.

This rough description will give some sense of the shadow patterns arising from a given plan. But the designer usually wants to make more exact studies, and for this there are tables available giving sun direction and altitude for different hours and seasons, at a given latitude. Or he may construct such a table for himself. From these, he may draw shadow contours, showing all the ground shaded during one given day, or even during an entire year. Or, using sun direction and altitude at turning points in the year, he may make an analysis in section of the relation between a significant building or outdoor area and the objects which will shade it: trees, eaves, screens, and structures.

Page 225

See below

One of the most comprehensive and graphic methods is to place a model of all the potential shadow-casting objects on a device which will simulate the sun direction for various times and seasons at that latitude. A simple way of doing this is to construct a cardboard dial with a central pointer, marking it with the sun's shadow path at different seasons for that latitude, in other words a crude sundial for the given place. Attach this sundial to the model with its meridian oriented to model north, and then, out in the sunlight, tip and tilt the base of the model until the pointer on the little sundial indicates the right hour and season. The sunlight is now falling on the model in the same way it would fall on the real object at that time and place. Bright artificial light may also be used if the source is over 10 feet away. Shadow patterns are given directly, and even the interior lighting of rooms may be studied if window openings are to scale.

Page 223

The control of noise outdoors is a special subject in itself, and little work has been done on it, since attention has
been concentrated on interior acoustics. Although an environment with too little noise is conceivable, the usual
problem is to reduce either the noise level or the information
content of the noise. Sound sources are increasingly powerful and ubiquitous.

References 37 and 41

Noise levels are measured in decibels, a logarithmic scale
which is one at the threshold of hearing, and 140 at the
threshold of pain. Each interval of ten decibels indicates a
level of sound energy ten times greater than before, an
increase which the human ear may distinguish as being
roughly twice as loud. A noise twenty decibels higher than
another has one hundred times the energy of the latter, and
so on. For example, various sources scale roughly as follows:

Decibels

10	quiet rustle of leaves
20–30	soft whisper
40	hum of a small electric clock
50	ambient noise, house kitchen
60	normal conversation
70–80	busy street
90–100	subway close at hand, or a piano
110–120	auto horn or a pneumatic hammer
160	jet airplane

In most areas, we should like to keep noise levels down
to 50 or 60 decibels, and down to 30 decibels just outside
rooms devoted to study or sleep, if they are to be allowed
the luxury of open windows. But noises are annoying or noticeable as much because of their frequency, or pitch, as
because of their level of loudness. Thus high-pitched noises,
or ones whose frequencies blanket the frequencies of human
speech, will be particularly obnoxious. Sounds whose pitch
contrasts sharply with the background noise will be picked
up even if they are relatively soft. The frequency of noises
audible to the human ear will usually range between 20 and
20,000 cycles per second, or 50 and 10,000 cycles at low
noise levels. Ordinary street noises range in frequency from
about 40 to 8000 cycles per second, while most human speech
is transmitted in the 100 to 3000 cycle range.

Outdoor sounds are attenuated in many ways before
reaching the receiver. The most useful means available to a
site planner is simply the attenuation due to the spreading
of sound as it travels from the source. Each doubling of the
distance between source and receiver causes sound levels to

drop by six decibels. That is, noise decreases as the square of the distance from a point source. But from a linear source, such as a highway, it decreases only directly as the distance and thus sound levels may drop only about 3 decibels for each doubling of distance. To prevent the annoying transmission of speech, openable windows should not be closer than 30 to 40 feet apart if face-to-face, nor 6 to 10 feet if on the same wall plane.

Sound is dispersed by turbulence and gusty winds. Sound shadows may be produced upwind of noise sources even with gentle steady winds, if the air close to the ground is warmer and is moving more slowly. Then sound waves are deflected upwards, and there may be a zone of quiet for 200 to 2000 feet upwind. These effects cannot be depended upon, however.

Barriers of planting or structure will also reduce sound transmission. Belts of trees are only partly useful, being most efficient against the noises of high frequency, whose wavelengths are not much larger than the average size of leaves and other obstacles they meet, i.e., noises of over 10,000 cycles per second. Tests have indicated that a thousand feet of woods, thick enough to limit visibility to 70 feet, will decrease noise in the 200–1000 cycles per second range by only about 20 decibels more than would the open distance alone.

Solid barriers — earth, walls, buildings — are more effective. If the barrier is relatively impenetrable to sound, the noise reaching the receiver is what has passed around the barrier. The effectiveness of the barrier, relative to no barrier at all, increases as barrier height increases, as it is moved closer to either source or receiver, and as the frequency of the emitted sound increases. Thus a high wall close to the source will reduce high frequency noise markedly, while a low wall, half-way between source and receiver, has little effect on low-frequency sound.*

Finally, outdoor noise is absorbed to some extent by ground and wall surfaces, so that the use of nonreflective

* More precisely, a solid barrier reduces noise levels (in addition to the reduction by distance) by the number of decibels,

$$D = 10 \sqrt[6]{\frac{30h^2(a+b)}{\lambda\,ab}}.$$

Reference 46

In this formula, h is the height of the barrier above the line between source and receiver, a is the distance in feet from source to barrier, b is the distance from receiver to barrier, and λ is the wavelength of the sound in feet (λ equals 1130 divided by the frequency of the sound in cycles per second). This calculation is valid where source and receiver are on the ground, and approximately level.

textures will have an effect in reducing sound levels. But it is difficult to make artificial surfaces which are both weatherproof and also sufficiently fine textured to be efficient sound absorbers. Snow and fine-grained natural vegetative covers are somewhat effective. If noise levels cannot be brought down to an acceptable point, it is often useful to mask the noise by adding desirable or random sound: the play of water, music, the rustle of leaves, even "static" or "white noise."

Thus the site planner puts his reliance on the avoidance or suppression of noise sources, or on separating activities from them by substantial distances. His next defense is to use buildings or other solid objects as partial barriers to sound transmission, or to increase the background noise to mask out annoying intrusions or to reduce their information content. As a last stand, he completely seals his buildings, and abandons the outdoors.

Urban Climate

Man has profoundly modified the microclimate over much of the earth. He has simplified it, reducing contrasts by his drainage, forest clearance, plowing, and planting of standard crops. He has also made a new microclimate, that of the city, which is the result of the extensive paving, the dense structures, and the emission of heat, noise and impurities. In general, urban areas are warmer, dustier, drier, and yet foggier than their rural counterparts. The noise level is higher; there is glare and added air pollution; wind velocities are lower. Wind speeds at street level may be one-third of free wind speeds. All of these make for a definite "city climate," which constitutes one of the chief popular criticisms of city life. But once we understand the nature of microclimatic effects, it should be possible to make the urban climate better than the rural one, rather than the reverse. Manipulation of surfaces and structures, and the use of direct artificial devices (refrigerated or heated panels, fans, water sprays) may produce climates more desirable than any "natural" alternative.

The site planner can use climatic information in the choice of site, predicting how the general climate will interact with the detailed form of the locality. Once he is aware of the substantial possibilities of variation in microclimate, he will use many sources beside his own judgment to evaluate a locality: the evidence of older construction and its weathering and adjustment to site, the knowledge of old residents, or the evidence of existing plant cover. The types of plants, and particularly their health, rate of development, and budding time, are sensitive indices of fine variations in climate.

The designer will have certain situations in mind which he tends to avoid or to make special provision for: steep north slopes, west slopes facing water, hilltops, frost pockets or positions at the foot of long open slopes, bare dry ground, nearby sources of noise or air pollution. There will be other situations that he will be attracted by, such as middle slopes facing southeast to southwest, locations near water, well-planted areas, and so on.

But even more important, he will use his knowledge of climate to change the local weather. Having evaluated his site in relation to the general climate, he will orient his structures to take maximum advantage of sun, shade, and prevailing winds. He will produce shade at the right spots by means of trees or artificial structures, and channel or divert the wind or cold air floods with buildings and planting. He will select surface materials for their albedo or for their sound absorption, erect barriers to noise, or establish pleasant noises to mask out undesirable ones. Neglect of these factors is bound to produce a worsening of climate in the act of building. Attention to them, even with our present incomplete knowledge, can improve it substantially.

It remains true, however, that we have much to learn about climate, particularly about its application to the art of site planning. The original studies of the microclimate were concerned with agricultural problems, and the field of acoustics has concentrated on interior noise control. The outdoor effects of man-made structures and materials are not yet well understood, and there is not much quantitative data that a designer can use in a precise way. Nor is there any large-scale systematic recording of the microclimate in urban and suburban areas. Considering its importance for comfort and health, should not a planner have microclimatic and acoustic data on a locale about to be developed, just as he has topographic, sub-soil, and utility information as a matter of routine?

Chapter 7

Problems of Control

Sometimes a site planner can exercise no more than partial control over the environment. This occurs in the layout of subdivisions, in the preparation of long-range site plans, and in the control of future site planning. Although these three activities are quite distinct, they share the same qualities of incompleteness and indeterminancy, and are thus worth discussing and comparing together.

Subdivision

Subdivision is the process whereby vacant land is divided into lots and public rights-of-way, providing sites for future individual buildings which will occupy those lots when they have been transferred to other developers. This process may or may not be accompanied by the actual provision of roads, paths, utilities, and landscaping. Subdivision is a common method of putting land to use for low-density residential development; it is used occasionally for other purposes, such as industry, agriculture, or even commerce. It is a technique of long history, which lies behind most urban development throughout the world.

In planning a subdivision, the designer controls the position of roads, paths, and utilities, the location of public facilities and public open space, the shape and position of lots, and perhaps also such features as landscaping, grading, and detail. But he can influence the siting and planning of buildings only indirectly, and thus his plan must be studied without simultaneous consideration of the architecture.

Since in an urban setting the buildings are crucial, this means that the subdivider can only speculate how site and architecture will fit into each other. The division of work might be analogous to asking one man to set canvas size, design the frame, and indicate the principal abstract shapes in a painting, while asking another to paint the picture. Skilled men can sometimes override such unnatural divisions, but the results are often undistinguished or even disastrous.

This technique may operate fairly well where the character and siting of buildings is prescribed by custom, but it is much more dangerous when design traditions are weak and technical possibilities very numerous. Emphasis must be placed on circulation and on property boundaries, with a neglect of spatial effect and a lack of coordination between internal and external design. In reviewing subdivision plans, it is possible to pick out those which will result in disorder or poor living conditions, but it is quite difficult to separate distinguished from simply indifferent designs.

Nevertheless, there are reasons why development by subdivision continues to be employed. First and most important, subdivision of a large tract does not require so much capital as complete development of land. The subdivider need only invest in the land, its survey, and its legal division. He may also, in some cases, put in roads and utilities, and perform the grading and landscaping. In either case, subdivision is typically the device of a modest economy, with small and scattered capital accumulation. Second, subdivision decentralizes decision, relieving the developer of architectural design and allowing later owners to exercise some choice about their structures. Third, it is well suited to a slow tempo of development, allowing land to be put to use piecemeal as demand develops, and permitting governmental agencies to exercise control over general development without being asked to make similar deliberations each time a building is proposed.

For all these reasons subdivision has social advantages despite its adverse effect on site planning quality. Therefore it becomes important to know what can be done in such situations and how the process might better be accomplished in the future. It is a strategic juncture at which a designer can often achieve a permanent effect quite easily.

Good subdivision design can prevent the worst. It can insure good circulation, adequate facilities, sufficient open space, and a basic order. These flow from the general principles of design discussed previously. Since the circulation system, at least, is concretely provided for, it may be designed and tested by all the criteria discussed in Chapters 4 and 11: principles of flow, social communication, and visual effect, plus technical standards for horizontal and vertical alignment, and for intersections, turn-arounds, block length, rights of way, pavement widths, and so on. The road pattern should conform to the general circulation plan for the area, and provide for future roads and connections. It is customary to say that rights of way should be 50 feet wide as a minimum, and this may be necessary where little future control can be exercised. But widths of 35 feet may sometimes be sufficient. The first basic test for any subdivision plan is to move in imagination through its streets, checking its technical, social, and esthetic quality.

Reference 36

Pages 37 and 176

The second fundamental test is to arrange a hypothetical building on each lot, making sure that each lot has at least one good location for a structure. Thus a typical one-story single-family house may be tried out on each lot, if this is the building type expected.

Rules are often stated regarding acceptable widths, depths, or proportions of lots, but the placement of a building is the real test. If sufficient access, outdoor space, privacy, and view can be achieved with a normal building, then the shape and size of a lot are up to standard. The mimimum lot frontages commonly used in contemporary subdivision regulations often impose uneconomic or monotonous designs. Ways need to be found to abandon these rules, without allowing substandard arrangement of buildings. Given current single-family houses in the normal disposition to the street, a rectangular lot is usually most efficient, and will have a width at the street of at least 50 feet. But if row houses or patio houses or other types of layouts are employed, these standards lose their force.

Lots are becoming wider at the street and shallower in depth, shifting from the traditional 50 by 150 foot standard for single-family houses to something like 75 by 100 feet. This width accommodates the one-story "ranch" house, and minimizes the depth of the dark side yards. But it is more expensive, since street frontage is a principal cost element, and it reduces any privacy in the back yard. With present house types and customary setbacks, the minimum lot depth should probably be 120 feet. A lot twice as deep as it is wide is likely to allow reasonable outdoor activity in relation to a typical contemporary house. There is something to be said for the old narrow, deep lot, with its low cost and privacy at the rear.

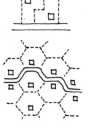

Lots nearly rectangular in shape, which avoid any acute-angled corners, are easier to develop. A common rule prescribes that side lot lines should be perpendicular to the street lines, to avoid waste of land and a saw-tooth arrangement of façades along the block. Yet all these rules depend on the building arrangement and may be superfluous. Special lot shapes have been experimented with, such as circles, hexagons, or interlocking "L"s or "T"s, and they may have advantages in some conditions. No rule requires all lots to be of uniform size.

Building lines, or limits within the lot lines beyond which a structure may not protrude, are often made part of a subdivision plan. These may be private contractual restrictions, or they may reflect controls prescribed by law. They further restrict the site, and must be taken into account in checking the "buildability" of a lot. While their primary purpose is to insure privacy, access, and sufficient light and air, they may also be used for visual effect, causing the street fronts to advance or recede, or the spaces to open or close. Where voluntarily imposed, they need not be uniform. Enclosing lots in a mechanical and restrictive set of front, side, and rear set-back lines results in a uniform building location on each lot. This uniformity gives a monotonous "dentellated" effect as it is repeated down the street.

The final basic test that may be applied to the design of a subdivision is to see that adequate reservation has been made for such facilities as schools, parks, playgrounds, churches, and shopping. These areas should be well located and adequate in size and quality, following the principles noted in Chapters 3 and 9.

Subdivision Character

By giving thought to the street pattern, to the usefulness of lots, and to the provision of sites for community use, the designer of a subdivision may insure basic functional adequacy and create an underlying order, thereby forestalling some of the worst consequences of a bad site plan. He can also do a little more to give the area a positive visual character. His strongest resource is the street and path system, since it is while moving along these ways that his development will be seen. Thus the sequence and dynamic shape of the roads, the way they point or lead to the more intensive uses, and their relation to the building lines along their course, can have a visual impact on the observer.

The disposition of intensive uses and public lands can create focal points and open reaches. Lot and building lines may within limits be employed to vary setbacks and create building clusters. Lot location and shape may be used to encourage buildings at desired points, such as at the head of a cul-de-sac for visual closure, or on the end of a narrow block to prevent the usual long view down back yard fences. Finally, the landscaping may be used to convey a general character, or even, by going beyond the customary obsession with street trees, to create a general visual structure.

It remains true, however, that the subdivision method is an unnatural disruption of the design process, and that lack of coordination between site and architectural design inevitably blurs and coarsens the final product. It would be worthwhile to try to avoid this division. For example, it might be possible for a general subdivision plan to deal only with major streets, use locations, and principal landscaping, leaving minor paths, lots, and other details to be planned in small areas as actual buildings were demanded and designed. This is the procedure generally followed in industrial land subdivision, where lots are rarely fixed before a buyer and his building requirements are known.

Long-Range Site Planning

Somewhat similar to the problem of subdivision is the process of long-range site planning: the preparation of plans for growth twenty years or even further into the future. Such planning is possible for a large and stable organization, occupying a permanent site, subjected to protracted growth, and able to exercise long-term control and direction. A university, a hospital, or a large manufacturing plant are examples of this type of client.

The problem is like subdivision in that the future uses and their building envelopes are not precisely known, although a general plan for land improvement, circulation and use location is required. It differs from subdivision in that the agency for whom the plan is being made will also eventually control the building design. The agency can therefore develop long-range policy and will be able to revise its general plan in the future. Thus, however abstract it may be, long-range site planning is a legitimate and useful exercise. It occupies a natural division in the design scale of increasing area and time, and is not, like subdivision, an artificial separation of what should be a unitary design process.

This is not meant to deny the difficulty of long-range site planning. Not only is building shape unknown, but so is anything more than generalized future use. Such a design must normally be preceded by planning studies of future growth and function, and future trends in the environs, which lie beyond the scope of this text. Long-range site planning is, indeed, a half-way house between site and city planning.

Once future growth and function have been predicted, and preferred density and land requirements determined, then a generalized future site plan must be prepared. This will consist at least of a land use and major circulation pattern. Since some guide to future physical form is also desirable, it has been customary to prepare a normal site plan showing building shapes fixed for the ensuing twenty years. Masses are simplified, and precise designations are left off the structures. Detailed adjustment is relied upon to meet future needs.

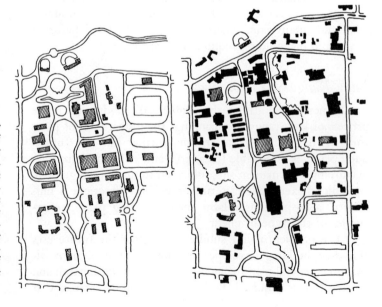

Figure 25 *Plan for the University of California campus at Berkeley, officially adopted in 1914, and the actual development in 1956* (*Source:* Long-Range Development Plan for the Berkeley Campus, *University of California, August 1956*).

Such plans of future building shapes have been universal failures. Sometimes they have been abandoned very quickly; at other times they have been maintained for a while and then gradually slurred over and finally forgotten in the course of time. Occasionally they have been stoutly maintained and defended, until at last the strain of misplaced function has become intolerable, and the plan has been abruptly if regretfully discarded. In most large institutions, the pace of functional change is too rapid to allow the fixing of the structural envelope very far into the future.

Can anything be projected, beyond general use, density, and the circulation pattern? While these will insure orderly functional development, they have only a secondary effort on the visual form of the future complex. Complete reliance must then be put on the skill of the designers of individual buildings, who at best will produce structures in harmony with their immediate neighbors. Only by chance can a visual form develop which will be apparent at the larger scale of the whole. A form created at this larger scale in advance of a specific program has rarely been successful. We need to know far more about how it can be done. What examples we have, however, furnish us with a few clues.

As in subdivision design, the character of the path system may be set in advance. The sequence of views as the observer enters and passes through may be considered, the paths and their directions made identifiable by landscaping and detail, and the whole network shaped into a clearly visible interlocking structure. It is possible at times to make the path system the dominant impression, with individual structures strung along it as incidents.

It is also possible to determine the major spatial form well in advance of construction. This is most simply and commonly done by the reservation of open areas, such as plazas and parks. Street spaces, or edges of development, may also be defined by setting building and height lines that will have strong visual effect regardless of detailed design. Large plants or plant masses may create spaces independent of the buildings. Spaces so created may then be linked into a total system in relation to the path structure.

Instead of defining the exact spatial form, it may even be possible to prescribe a general spatial character, such as recommending a continuous network of small courts linked by short tunnels. Instead of precisely mapping the location of these future courts and tunnels, new construction would simply be tested for conformity to this general but explicit pattern. Harmonious spatial continuities of this kind, which give a strong character to the whole, are illustrated in many old towns where tradition, rather than explicit plan, was the guide.

The structure of spaces and paths is probably the principal tool by which the long-range site planner can shape the visual form. But there are others as well: he can lay out the major landscaping, using dominant plant types to give areas particular character, or using large specimens or concentrations to mark out the key paths and nodal points. He may prescribe the skyline profile, or the points at which major architectural accents will be allowed. He may at times go further in limiting future construction by suggesting materials, color, texture, the character of fenestration, or even the nature of massing or detail. He will use just that level of control which will confer character and continuity, while imposing a minimum of restriction on the shape and function of future structures.

His plan, therefore, instead of being a somewhat abstracted site drawing, will consist of a plan of land use, circulation, and major space, supplemented by diagrams, statements, and illustrative details which will guide the character of future growth. Like any large-scale, long-range plan, this cannot be fixed for all time, but must be subject to constant revision and development. A great deal, however, must be done to refine the technique of this sort of work.

See diagram of long-range form, page 112

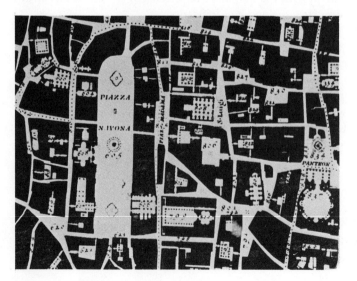

FIGURE 26 *A portion of Nolli's map of Rome, 1748, showing the continuous interconnection of interior and exterior spaces.*

FIGURE 27 *District spatial character: an aerial view of Trinity College, Cambridge.*

Site Controls

Both the subdivision and the long-range plan involve the question of control: the achievement of continuity and the prevention of inferior work by means of regulation rather than design. Such controls, imposed either by official agency as an ordinance, or by private agency as a covenant, have been shown to be absolutely necessary if we are to avoid the worst aspects of congestion, disorder, and ugliness. These controls are widely accepted as limitations on use, density, and the layout of circulation. They are viewed with greater suspicion when applied to visual form.

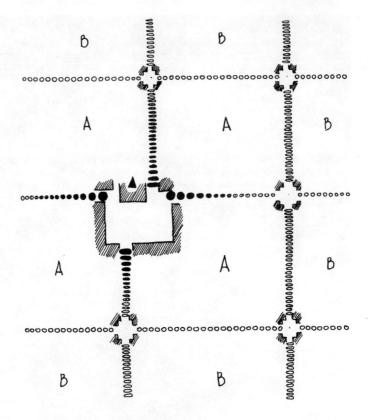

FIGURE 28 *An imaginary diagram for the control of long-range visual form.*

The letters indicate regions of future building. *"A" might refer to a region where the buildings are to be two to four stories high, at high ground coverage, of prescribed wall texture, surrounding small interconnected courts. The typical character of such courts could be illustrated in accompanying sketches. "B," on the other hand, might refer to a region where structures could be sited more freely, within a given range of floor area ratio, and subject to certain general rules for interspacing.*

The linear symbols indicate pathways of two distinct types, differentiated by planting and paving. The cross sections and elevations of these paths are prescribed, as well as their landscaping, lighting, signing, and detail. Darkening of the symbol indicates a recommended increase in spatial constriction, and in the apparent intensity of activity and detail along the path.

The central open space would be precisely located in plan and section, and there is a mandatory building line, a cornice height, and a façade treatment. The path intersections are to be defined by planting or structure, according to a typical section. The black triangle locates a tall landmark.

In addition to sketches of the various spatial forms, the diagram would be accompanied by specifications and illustrative detail as to prescribed or recommended planting, paving, furniture, fences, signs, and lighting, as well as the colors, textures, and fenestration of walls.

Controls are negative and passive measures as opposed to the positive technique of direct design. They tend to stifle innovation and restrict individual freedom; in a world of skill and good will they might be unnecessary. They have the characteristics of any negative means: they can prevent the worst but rarely bring about the best. If not used with restraint, they will produce an environment of competent mediocrity.

Yet controls are necessary. The trick is to use them as sparingly as will achieve the end in view, and to review their efficacy periodically. Certain proven kinds of control leave many dimensions of freedom to the individual. Density controls are of this type, since density has a fundamental technical, social, economic, and even visual impact, and yet when fixed still allows a great variety of building envelopes. Control over the street system is another useful and accepted example of regulation. Limitation on land use is also widely practiced and makes fundamental sense when applied in a general way. On the other hand, very precise use controls and the strict avoidance of use mixtures may be unnecessarily rigid. It may be preferable to control some uses by setting up performance standards to control nuisance effects, or by prescribing the intensity of use rather than the type.

Building lines, both in plan and elevation, are commonly used, but they are often applied with little thought. If the objective is to control density or to insure light and air, then there are other more flexible ways of attaining the same ends. In subdivisions, standard building lines often reduce the buildable area of lots to small, choppy, spatial forms. The principal value of the building line is either to achieve a visual effect, or to reserve certain areas of ground. It is not necessary to set building lines with monotonous uniformity; they may be drawn to produce spatial coherence and variegated character. Occasionally in key locations it may be desirable to set minimum, as well as maximum, lines.

Other controls may refer to the detailed quality and design of components, such as specifications for roads or utilities. Sometimes controls deal with building materials, or details such as signs, planting, and fences. Occasionally, and this is more dangerous, they will refer to design or style. All of these may have unforeseen results. There must be some mechanism for future modification of the controls, whether by action of a central agency such as a board of trustees or a government, or by provision that the controls will lapse at a specified time and must then be renewed.

At times, controls have been designed for their secondary effects. Developers may be required to install expensive improvements, for example, in order to block or slow down their operations, or density or minimum house sizes may be set to exclude certain income levels. This is dangerous ground. Direct exclusion of race or class has now happily been struck down as an enforceable device.

More legitimate are the special powers of exception, which allow control bodies to release developers from certain onerous restrictions in return for some quid pro quo of space, density, or design excellence. Designers may thus be able to exceed density maxima at certain spots while keeping gross density low, or may be able to mix building types or uses while maintaining the objectives of zoning exclusions.

In dealing with the difficult problems of design control, one useful technique is the establishment of a board of review to which all designs must be submitted, but which has only persuasive power. It may also be appropriate to set up a local association of owners to exercise some of these controls and to maintain and operate common facilities such as parks, pools, planting, walkways, streets, sewage disposal, or water supply plants. Municipal agencies, however, may be jealous of such local power, or be concerned that such associations may not have the permanency to carry out their functions over a long period of time.

Chapter 8

The Process of Site Planning

Site planning may now seem unmanageably complex, to judge from all the factors involved. On the contrary, the elements of the art are as manageable as those of any other. Perhaps the most useful way to summarize these elements is to describe the process of site planning design.

The design should begin with the analysis of the two underlying parameters: site and purpose. Site analysis, which may be preceded by site selection, starts with a general unoriented reconnaissance, continues through a systematic check of factors of suspected significance, and ends with an analysis leading to a concise statement of the site's essential character and its major problems and potentialities.

Parallel with this analysis, a statement of objectives should be prepared, a step which is too often a rationalization after the fact. These objectives should be stated as concretely as possible, without dictating any particular physical solution.

Site and objectives cannot be studied independently but only in relation to each other, the purposes indicating what aspects of the site are relevant, and the site analysis influencing the goals which are possible or desirable. The statement of site and purpose will also be modified throughout the development of the design, since the design process is itself an exploration of site and goal possibilities. Despite this circularity, the first-round analysis of situation and purpose is the beginning step.

Site and purpose are always specific and particular and can never be assumed as standard. There are, however, certain general site factors which are almost always important in development, including such elements as subsurface condition, topography, climate, and the existing patterns of land use and circulation. Similarly, there are some basic human goals which very often appear in any statement of objectives: communication, choice, cost, health, adaptability, imageability. They will be supplemented by the direct technical objectives inherent in the original problem.

These are highly generalized aims which must be stated in much more precise form. Yet they are useful checks against the omission of important factors. Along with other purposes which may be germane to a particular problem, they should be evaluated as a total system, with some indication of relative weight, since most goals are in conflict with some other goals.

Next a detailed program is prepared, springing from basic objectives and resources, and influenced by the site and the knowledge of technical possibilities. It furnishes a quantitative schedule of facilities to be provided in the new development, and may be modified as design proceeds.

It is also customary at this time to review other site plans of similar objectives, in publications but especially on the ground, to see how they fitted plan to purpose, and with what success. This is not done in the spirit of imitation, although there is no reason why good forms should not be imitated, but to prepare the mind with criteria and alternatives for the creative process to come.

The Design of a Complex Whole

When both site and purpose are understood, and the preliminary program is in hand, the site planner then proceeds to the heart of the matter, which is the development of the design itself. Like any creative process, this is difficult to describe. It becomes particularly difficult in site planning, where the factors to be dealt with are so numerous.

However varied the factors involved, the site plan deals in its essence with three fundamental patterns of location in space: the pattern of activity, the pattern of circulation, and the visual form. These are the subject matter of first sketches and remain dominant themes throughout the work. Their nature has been explored in the preceding chapters. A site planner's stock in trade is his knowledge of a broad range of alternatives for these three patterns.

The designer is therefore faced with a multitude of interlocking possibilities. The difficulty lies in finding ways of treating as an interdependent whole a set of decisions which at first seem too numerous to grasp. It is often useful at first to make a piecemeal attack, reserving final judgment until the problem is seen as a whole. The planner may begin by studying some possible alternatives of the use pattern. Then he will drop these studies and go on to the analysis of circulation, and thence of form. By alternating between these factors, he gains an insight into their possibilities and can begin to pick up points of conflict and support, until at last he is dealing, even if only in a very loose way, with the three elements simultaneously.

Similarly, it is useful to deal first with a single objective at a time: to make some sketches to show the cheapest plan possible, or the most flexible, regardless of their implications for other valued ends. Here again, a partial analysis lays the groundwork for simultaneous study.

Modular Design

Still another useful breakdown between part and whole is on an areal basis. The designer may begin by quick sketches for over-all patterns of the whole, alternating with other sketches for the development of small units of the development. The alternating sketches at first proceed independently of each other and are only gradually built into total systems.

The unit of development chosen for the study of parts, a unit which might be called a module, should be small enough to be developed as a totality without unreasonable effort and to be repeated a number of times throughout the total plan. It must be large enough, on the other hand, to coincide with some of the important design issues, such as spatial form or social grouping. Thus in a large housing development, a module of one or two houses might miss all the important issues of interrelation, while a module of 500 houses would offer little design convenience over a study of the whole, as well as being so large as to be unrepeatable and inadaptable to variations in terrain. In low density housing work, a module of ten to twenty houses is often a convenient one.

Study at the level of the module necessarily includes the internal organization of the structures as well as their external relations. The use, form, and circulation of the buildings must dovetail into the use, form, and circulation of the site. Therefore the building and its setting are best designed together. There are some exceptions as noted in the preceding chapter, and it may not be necessary to carry the architectural design out to complete detail while organizing the site. But the main lines of the architecture and the site design should be developed simultaneously, whether by one man or by a closely cooperating team. Alternative site and building solutions must be judged together, and neither one can dictate the final solution.

For all its usefulness in the design process, the modular approach should not be elevated from a design convenience to a design principle. Some sites are best planned as a series of repeating units, others are not. The purpose of the study of modules is not to insure a modular design, but only to provide an entering wedge leading into the study of large complexes. As the designer begins to take command of detail through his initial modular study, he will advance to a study of the whole, where modular repetition may be completely abandoned.

All these approaches — modular analysis, plans for single objectives, isolated studies of use, form, or circulation — are design techniques leading up to the study of complex wholes. The alternation of attention from part to part,

FIGURE 29 *An early study by John R. Myer for the Government Center, Boston. Building mass, open spaces, grades, circulation, paving, and detail are all being developed together in the context of the existing city.*

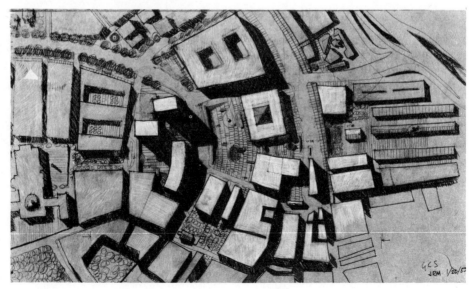

FIGURE 30 *An early sketch by Sven Markelius for the Lincoln Center, New York City, in which he faces the buildings on an internal square, one level above the surrounding streets. Rapid and free, the sketch deals with the essentials in plan and section.*

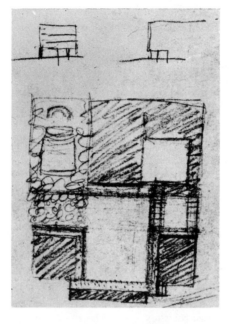

while judgment is reserved, prepares the mind for studies in which the significance of each decision is instantly understood in every important dimension. This simultaneous mastery of the whole, which is essential to an integrated plan, takes time to achieve. When it is attained, it will seem that each trial modification of the developing plan immediately reacts on the remainder of the design in all its aspects. The designer will begin to imagine total systems, sharp and precise at the critical points, looser and unresolved where decisions have less significance for the whole. He will begin to weigh such total systems against each other, rather than comparing fractional alternatives.

The studies themselves should be carried out in various forms. Plans and sections are essential. Perspective sketches are also useful. Almost always it is advisable to make model studies, since the designer is dealing with decisions in three dimensions. Unfortunately, models are not sufficient in themselves, because they are imprecise, they falsify detail, and they take time to build.

Reason and Unreason

The studies proceed in the schizophrenic manner common to all design: the planner is at times relaxed and uncritical, allowing his subconscious mind to suggest new forms and connections, most of them completely fantastic and un-workable. At other times he looks sharply at these suggestions, consciously testing them for the way in which they apply to his purposes. Thus he is involved in another alternating process: a swing from almost automatic doodling, in which ideas and forms seem to develop "of themselves," to a sternly critical review of each new suggestion. Part of the skill of a designer lies in managing these two states of mind so that, on the one hand, his critical powers do not inhibit creative suggestion, while on the other his irrrational processes do not prevent adequate analysis.

Large numbers of form possibilities must be turned out in a state of mind as free from prejudice and practicality as possible. When, on looking back, one or two of these suggestions seem to have some possibility of use, however remote, they are then fully developed in sketch form. These sketches may be developed quickly, in a loose free style, but should be complete, fixing all major aspects. Alternatives should not be "worked over" by constant modification and erasure: they should be developed, set aside, and redrawn as complete systems. Otherwise, potentially valuable possibilities will be buried under layers of partial changes. A good designer knows where his sketch can be vague, and where it must be precise, that is, where he can reserve judgment and neglect detail and where he must test the key decisions.

In this way a series of alternative possibilities is developed, covering as wide a range as possible, which can then be tested in comparison with each other. Certain alternatives will be rejected, others retained for further trial and development, and yet more new ones will be suggested in the process. The designer will redraw feasible alternatives several times, modifying them to meet various objections. But he must know when to abandon this process, when to reject totally some scheme which has been so overlaid with compromises as to lose all its original force and clarity. He will also be alert to catch the hint of some totally new arrangement which appears momentarily in this troubled shifting of forms, being quick to extract it and start afresh. Final decisions on the basic scheme will be made as the alternatives narrow down, and as the designer begins to see the whole complex in all its significant dimensions simultaneously.

The design process should be kept as open and fluid as possible until a wide range of alternatives has been developed and tested. All too often this process is cut short by a state

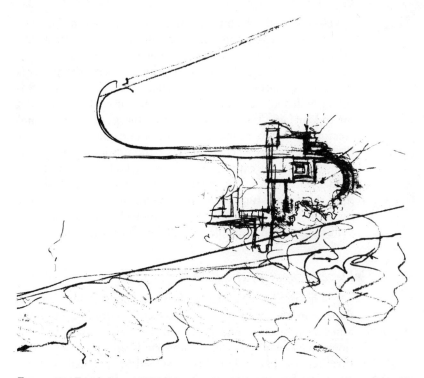

FIGURE 31 *Frank Lloyd Wright's sketch for the Booth house. Inside and outside, building and site are dealt with as one (from Frank Lloyd Wright:* Drawings for a Living Architecture, *published for the Bear Run Foundation Inc. and the Edgar J. Kaufman Charitable Foundation by Horizon Press, 1959).*

of mind which is narrow and critical from the beginning, as though design were a logical process which proceeded from initial assumptions by rational steps to a unique solution. On the contrary, design is an irrational search, conducted over a ground previously prepared by experience, the study of principles, and the analysis of site and purpose. It is after this search has produced the alternative possibilities that rational criticism is brought to bear. Every plan should be preceded by great numbers of discarded sketch alternatives. Every designer should be haunted by the fear that he has left some alternative untried. Even when a final alternative has been selected, it is wise to allow some time to elapse before confirming this choice. The designer has an emotional attachment to plans that arise in the heat of design. Several days later, such plans may appear to be surprisingly weak.

In summary then, the design process in which the basic site plan is determined consists of a large number of sketch studies, which proceed gradually from partial aspects to a simultaneous treatment of the whole pattern in all its major dimensions, and which typically alternate between bursts of unconscious suggestion, and the rational development and criticism of feasible alternatives. These studies finally result in a sketch general plan, dealing primarily with the patterns of activity, circulation, and visual form. Normally, this sketch will show building location and form, the circulation on the surface, the use of all areas, the general shape and treatment of the ground, the major landscaping, and any additional features which will affect the outdoor space. This decision will be expressed in plan, in section, in a sketch model, and often in perspective or isometric views. The plan may show only ultimate development, or it may indicate a series of stages by which this is reached, each stage being viable in itself and capable of enduring for some time.

Development of the Plan

This preliminary plan is then developed in its technical dimension and in its details. The sketch will have left some aspects unresolved, and there will be many details to consider: pavement textures, minor landscaping, street furniture, fences. These should be designed or specified, and not left to be furnished by traditional means, if a handsome and useful environment is to result.

Substantial technical development must also be carried forward. Its principal elements are the precise alignment and specification of the road and walk system, the location and design of the utilities, and the grading plan. Again, it is only the detailed development of these features that is put off until this late period. In sketching the road system, the designer has already considered its technical demands. He has been aware of special problems he may have created in regard to utilities. He must already have evolved a general grading plan, since the shape of the ground is a key to the area's usefulness, drainage, maintenance, circulation, and appearance. Therefore it is less likely that detailed technical development will force any radical revision of the plans of an experienced designer, although this possibility cannot be ignored. Technical development is certain, however, to cause some significant modifications in the preliminary plan.

Practice differs in the extent to which technical development is carried out by the site planner before he turns the work over to an engineer. Ideally, the entire design process, down to the detailing of curbs and manholes, is pushed to completion in one office, which must then include a trained

References 45 and 47

civil engineer. At the opposite extreme, the site planner may go no further than the sketch general plan, leaving to an independent engineer the road and utility layout and the grading plan. But since these technical drawings are an essential part of the whole scheme, the site planner and the engineer must continue to make mutual adjustments; otherwise the intent of the plan will be thwarted, and the engineer will be forced into awkward solutions which could have been avoided by revision of the original plan.

The following discussion assumes a half-way position which is a fairly common one: the site planner prepares the sketch general plan, the general road and utility layout, and the grading and landscape plans, leaving to the engineer the precise alignments for the surveyor, the utility systems in detail, the road and walk cross sections and specifications, and the computations of earth balance.

Whatever division of duties is agreed upon, we would urge, as a minimum, that the site planner should prepare the sketch general plan, the landscape plan, and a freehand version of the grading plan. To do this, and to coordinate his work with the engineer, he must be capable of performing the work discussed below.

Road Layout

Technical development usually begins with a precise layout of the structures and paths shown on the sketch plan to the degree of accuracy required for their location on the site by contractors. This drawing involves reducing street layouts to circular curves and tangents and setting the precise geometry of building and property lines with relation to benchmarks and compass direction.

Accepted standards for the horizontal alignment of roads are given in Chapter 11. The freehand sketch of the road centerline is approximated as closely as possible by a succession of curves and tangents obeying these standards, or minor modifications are made. Station points are then marked on this precise centerline. This precise layout is primarily a mechanical step which only rarely reveals deficiencies in the plan but which sets the stage for further technical drawings.

Page 178

See below

The vertical dimension of the plan is then detailed. This usually begins with the design of the road profile. On a separate sheet of cross-section paper, a flattened-out, continuous section through ground at the centerline is drawn along each

Page 187

road (each consecutive run of station points.) The horizontal scale is that of the road layout; the vertical scale is usually ten times exaggerated. First the designer plots the existing surface along this line. Over this plot he then develops a new road profile as a succession of straight grades and vertical curves. Chapter 11 discusses the current standards governing these grades and curves.

Since it is normally advisable to avoid deep cuts and fills, the new profile is approximated in first trials by a series of straight tangents, keeping close to existing ground. The designer tries to find a series of tangents with grades neither too steep nor too flat, with positive drainage (no sag curves at points difficult to drain in the plan), a series that minimizes and balances the cut and fill. Once such an arrangement has been found, vertical curves are drawn at the intersections of tangents, and the profile is modified if difficulties develop. The profile is also checked in relation to the horizontal layout to judge the shape of the road in three dimensions. Care must also be taken that the profile is self-closing, that is, that the elevations are the same on different centerlines at points where they intersect.

More difficult is the relation of the profile to the as-yet-undeveloped grading plan. The balance of cut and fill visible on the profile is only a first, and sometimes a misleading, indication of total earthwork. Since the profile tends to generate the detailed grading plan, a significant criterion for this profile is that it facilitate the design of a good shape for the ground surface as a whole. In developing the profile, a skilled planner will usually be aware of how he is influencing the grading plan, but subsequent development of this plan will often force him to reconsider the profile.

Spot elevations at other critical points in the plan, such as the elevations of finished floor in the principal buildings, or those at the base of existing trees to be saved, are determined to the nearest tenth of a foot. They should be set to allow a workable grading plan and to conform with the sketch plan. These spot elevations and the elevations of road centerlines are then transferred to a precise layout on which existing contours have also been shown. The new contours of the road surfaces are then drawn in as far as the tops of the curbs. The road contours follow as a consequence of the

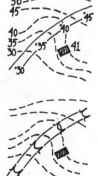

For road contours, see page 189

centerline profiles: the technique of drawing them is discussed in Chapter 11.

The Grading Plan

Next the grading plan itself is evolved, which will spec-
ify the new shape that the ground is to have when development is complete. This new shape is shown by drawing the
contours of the new ground surface where it will differ
from the existing surface. The new contours may be at five-,
two-, or one-foot intervals, depending on the scale of the
work. In conjunction with the existing contours, they indicate the degree of change, as well as the areas which will be
left undisturbed. While the grading plan, if a simple one,
may in the final contract documents be indicated only by
spot elevations at key points, it is essential to develop it as a
contour drawing in order to control the land form as a
whole. This plan is carried out in the field by erecting the
artificial structures (roads and buildings) to the levels
shown, and by setting grade stakes at intervals as required by
the new contours or spot elevations. The earth is then filled
up or cut down to indicated levels, while shaping the total
surface into a smooth curve between. Allowance should be
made for settling of fill, and for removal and replacement of
topsoil.

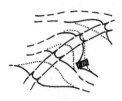

Figure 32, page 126

The grading plan is the most delicate and significant portion of the technical development. To achieve satisfactory
form, it often requires revision of the road and building elevations, or of the precise layout. Its implications sometimes
modify the basic plan itself. The skill with which it is done
will have much to do with the technical adequacy of the
plan, and also with its visual and functional success. It therefore requires care and time for proper development.

The grading plan must follow certain basic principles,
which the designer has had in mind from the beginning,
but which are now applied in detail. The ground surface
must, in the first place, be suitable for the intended use and
movement, and have a pleasing visual form. It is necessary to
look, in imagination, at the ground shapes being produced.
They will be ugly if carelessly done.

Chapters 3 and 5

The ground must also have positive drainage throughout, so that erosion and local flooding can be avoided. The
flow of drainage water from the sites upstream should not
be blocked, nor should the discharges on sites downhill be
increased. These rules are considered with the storm drainage system in Chapter 12.

Page 192

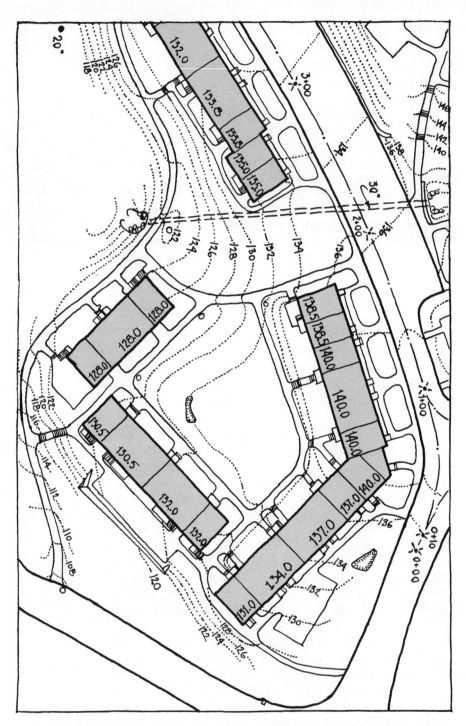

FIGURE 32 *Portion of a grading plan for a veterans' housing project in Waltham, Massachusetts (Olmsted Bros., landscape architects, Aldo Minotti, architect). This is the same site shown in the survey, Figure 5.*

In the normal case, the grading plan is kept as close to the previous natural grades as possible, since these usually represent a well-established equilibrium. Departures from this equilibrium upset the drainage pattern, expose or bury the roots of plants, disturb old foundations, and may produce visually awkward shapes. But where the ground is disturbed, it should be done so in a positive manner. Modern grading machinery requires broad, simple forms. Dabbling with the ground, producing fussy shapes or shallow cuts and fills, should be avoided. Sometimes the best plan calls for a dramatic disturbance of site such as shearing off a hill, or draining a river. Every effort should be made to conserve the agricultural value of the land, a resource which renews itself very slowly. Topsoil should be stripped, stockpiled, and replaced. Even then, the disturbance to the soil profile is serious, especially in cut. This is another reason for avoiding unnecessary shallow cuts.

Finally, for economy, the amounts of cut and fill should balance over the site, or within reasonable hauling distance, if the site is very large. This avoids the necessity for buying fill or disposing of cut. Sometimes, however, when on rocky land or poor soil, it may be found that a general filling of the land is the cheaper solution.

Estimating cut and fill is discussed on pages 218 and 219

As noted above, the grading plan begins with the new ground levels required at the foundations of structures, and at the curb lines of streets. In conformity with the stated principles and with the preliminary plan, new contours are drawn to make the transitions among these points, and between them and the existing ground surface.

It is most likely that the road profiles and the spot elevations of buildings will now have to be revised to make a good transition possible. The most common difficulties that develop are excessive or unbalanced cut and fill, which is costly and damaging to the land and its cover; drainage pockets in the land, on the roads, or against the sides of buildings; steep grades which may be dangerous, cause erosion, or make use, maintenance, or access difficult; a poor visual or functional relation between a building or a road and its immediate surroundings; and visually awkward transitions between one section and another.

Checking for these problems and eliminating them will be slow work until the designer has become skillful in reading contours on paper as if they were actual forms in space. The interspacing, linear quality, degree of parallelism, and

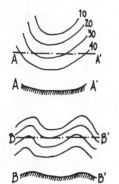

general pattern of these lines all have distinct meanings. It is useful to know that if one looks at any small part of a contour map with the lowest contours in that small part oriented to the top of the sheet, then one sees a series of exaggerated cross sections of the ground at that point.

This concept of the grading plan as an adjustment between rigid structures and the ground is the normal one, and justifiable in many circumstances. On other occasions, however, the designer may take a more positive attitude, considering the ground as a plastic material for abstract sculpture, with the aim of accomplishing more than just an harmonious, trouble-free adjustment. But in any case the general modelling of the ground surface will be an integral part of the general plan from the beginning.

Utilities and Details

When the grading plan has been completed, the layout of utilities is made, usually beginning with the storm drainage, which is the utility most likely to be significant. These studies should include, as a minimum, the plan layout of utility lines. At this time a check should be made to see that no critical problems of elevations or sizing will occur. *Page 192* The engineering of these utilities is discussed in Chapter 12. If the designer has been aware of these general implications, it is not likely that major revisions of the plan will be called for, although this may sometimes occur on detailed analysis. It is quite likely, however, that utility considerations will require changes in the precise layout or the grading plan, or will suggest more economical or functional dispositions.

The layout of all utilities may be shown on one sheet, or it may be more convenient to show the storm drainage on the grading plan, because it is so intimately related to topography. Depending on the extent to which engineering consultants will prepare construction drawings of their own, the utility plans may go beyond general layouts to show subsurface elevations and the sizing of conductors.

Finally, site details are specified, including the utility details noted above, pavement construction and finish, street furniture, and landscaping. Utility and road construction details and specifications, which are necessary contract documents, are likely to appear on the drawings of consultants, but they may appear in an integrated set of site drawings. Engineering services are usually required to prepare them except in the simplest cases.

Other details, such as landscaping, the finish of the ground plane, and street furniture, are commonly ignored or given only cursory notice. It has been one thesis of this text that they deserve the conscious attention of the site designer, and should appear in his drawings. Decisions as to landscaping, surface and wall materials, and the shape of minor structures and objects, may be shown on a landscape plan, which will be supplemented by partial sections, and by detailed drawings of special objects, such as fences, signs, utility poles, seats, steps, and fountains.

When technical development is complete, it must be checked for internal consistency and for compliance with the basic plan. The plan may be evaluated once more in the light of these findings, and readjusted. The technical drawings themselves, consisting most often of a precise surveying layout, a set of road profiles, a grading plan with spot elevations at key points, a utility layout, a landscape plan, and a sheet of details, are the "working drawings" of a site plan. Together with a set of specifications for pavements, utilities, grading and landscaping, they form the contract documents on which estimates and work can be based. These are the drawings needed to guide actual construction, but may not cover legal and administrative needs. For the latter purposes, requirements vary over the country, and include such items as plats for legal record, or plans for approval by public review agencies.

Drawings and Reports

Important as these technical drawings are, however, they are not the essence of the site plan. The essence can be found in the sketch, which may be a drawing, or a model, and which sets forth the pattern in three dimensions of the activity, circulation, and visual form. The correctness of this essential pattern will be tested, not simply by the technical finish of the detail, but especially by the way it conforms to essential purposes and to the spirit of the site.

The drawings will very often be accompanied, particularly in larger projects, with a written report that explains the reasoning behind the proposals and describes features which are more easily put in words. This need not describe the drawings, which should speak for themselves, nor simply be a colorful gloss on the proposals. Verbal and graphic expression are separate languages, both appropriate to convey different kinds of ideas, and should be employed where they are most useful. Designers will often tend to look on a report as "mere words" added after the real work is done, while laymen will think of the drawings as "mere pictures" which illustrate the report. Both groups are prejudiced by their unfamiliarity with one of the languages. The written or spoken word is often a necessity in conveying the principal ideas of a design to the client or the contractor.

The end product is not the report and the drawings, but the development on the ground. Thus it is not necessary that words and sketches do more than express the intent as accurately and articulately as possible. Excessive "finish" may actually confuse the client, and even the designer, as to what the end result will be. Willful distortions, such as the suppression of the surroundings or of incongruous detail, the falsification of light or of viewpoint, or the use of misleading language, are only too easy and common.

Finally, it will be important to supervise actual construction on the site, not only to insure compliance with the drawings, but also to make detailed adjustments as unexpected problems and opportunities arise. The ideal situation is to be able to study and modify a layout as it is staked out upon the ground, or even as it is under construction. This may be a rare opportunity in ordinary development, but should certainly be practiced at critical points wherever possible. Superintendence should be continuous wherever a development is long-range or takes time to mature. The effect in reality is the final arbiter of the plan.

II

Detailed Technique

Chapter 9

Housing

To consider detailed standards and patterns we must separate the general types of site planning, such as residential, commercial, industrial, and institutional. As the most common and fundamental kind of development, we will consider the planning of housing layouts in some detail. Other types of site planning, including those for unified shopping centers, for large institutions, and for industrial estates, are touched on more briefly in Chapter 10. As the discussion becomes more concrete, it will apply less and less generally. Much of the material in this chapter and in Chapter 10 is a reflection of American practice.

References 3, 22, 24, 27

Page 155

Based on the pattern which is normal to our own culture, the allocation of one family or one person to each dwelling unit (independent living quarters including cooking and bathing facilities) there are a number of common residential building types. They include:

1. *The single-family house:* each dwelling unit in its own isolated structure.

2. *The two-family house:* two units attached side by side.

3. *The row house:* three or more units attached side by side in a row.

4. *The flat or walk-up apartment:* single-story units stacked one above the other to a height of two, three, or, rarely, four or more stories, and accessible by common

stairs. The apartments may be paired side by side, with stairs between, or be grouped in threes, fours, or even more, around a central stair. These pairs or clusters may stand alone or be connected in lines. Alternatively, the apartments may open along a central corridor or an external gallery.

5. *Elevator apartments:* units stacked to greater heights and served by mechanical lifts, typically either of the slow speed type, resulting in heights of about six to seven stories; or the high speed type, allowing heights of 12 or more stories. Like walk-ups, elevator structures are most often either in a tower form ("point houses"), with three to six units clustered about a central elevator shaft, or in slab form, with units disposed along central or external corridors. The slabs may either be in straight lines, or be arranged in cross, "L," "H," "Y," or "Z" forms. The towers may be square in plan, or form crosses or "Y"s. The crosses or "Y"s can themselves be interlinked to form more complicated shapes.

These normal types have been listed in order of increasing density, and decreasing directness of access to street and ground. The first three allow for the provision of individual yards and independent access to each unit from the outside. Families with children between the ages of two and ten will usually prefer them.

The advantages of the one or two-story single-family house are well known: it has adequate light and air, and room for gardening, play, parking, and other outdoor uses; it enjoys direct access to the street and to its own private ground; it can be shielded from noise and view; it can be built, maintained, remodeled, bought, and sold independently; it symbolizes the individual family. It can be constructed at reasonable cost, although it is not the least expensive type of housing. Thus it is popularly considered to be the ideal house in many parts of the world. Its difficulties arise from the low densities it imposes, which may mean problems of city sprawl, poor transportation, sparse community services, and loss of rural land. It is only economical where land costs are low. If single-family houses must be used at net densities higher than five or six families per acre, then many of their advantages of space, privacy, individuality, and noise control begin to disappear. Except at very low densities, it is more difficult to compose small houses to make a coherent visual scene than it is to group larger units. Nevertheless, it seems clear that most new housing in the United States will be of this type, since it corresponds most closely to popular desire.

The two-family house, usually two stories high, is frequently used in parts of the eastern United States, and in England. It is cheaper than the single, can be built at higher densities, and provides opportunities either for individual ownership or for small scale investment and management, one side being owner-occupied and the other side rented out. Meanwhile, it retains many of the advantages of light and air, access, privacy, individual yards, and even some sense of individuality. Esthetically, it is no easier to handle than the single unit, and is likely to produce a similar dentellated effect at close densities.

The row house gives most space at lowest cost, and is the cheapest to maintain and heat. It will provide greater privacy than the single or two-family house on small lots, and makes much more efficient use of the land which would otherwise be dispersed in the narrow side yards. Each unit generally occupies about 20–35 feet of frontage and may be one, or more usually, two, stories high. It may be planned at densities which avoid the difficulties of urban sprawl, and at which adequate public transportation and community facilities can be provided. It is much easier to achieve coherent visual spaces with these continuous units, and very long rows, particularly if curving or bent to follow terrain or enclose an area, can be very dramatic.

All this is achieved at some sacrifice of individuality, although independent access and a private yard are retained. Noise control may be a problem, and care must be taken to insulate the party walls acoustically. Access to the rear yards from the street is troublesome, and must be allowed for by through passages (perhaps incorporating carports), or by rear alleys or short footways coming from the street or service yards. For this reason, it is now customary to put the kitchen and the service entrance on the street side of the unit, combined with the principal entrance. A neat service enclosure must then be incorporated with the front façade. For economy, it is best that a row contain an even number of dwellings, usually four, six, or eight together. Given its advantages, it is unfortunate that the row house has such an undeservedly poor reputation in this country.

The walk-up apartment was at one time the cheapest kind of housing available. It would still be so today, if either the fire laws had not banned the non-fireproof apartment, or if walk-up dwellings above the third floor were not popularly considered undesirable. Even the three-story walk-up is rarely built today, except where there are pressures for economy or high density, or where a public agency believes that subsidized units should be a little less than ideal, so that poor families will not loiter there. The two-story walk-up, however, is still a very useful type, since it provides the conveniences and freedoms of apartment living at low densities and at an intimate visual scale. Many units may still have private yards if desired. Parking and access is still easy. Units can be grouped about the stairs that so each one has good light and cross ventilation. These units may be very suitable for elderly couples, or for small or childless families. By increasing the ground coverage, relatively high densities and a special intimate and intense "urban" character may be achieved.

The elevator apartment is now, however, the normal response to a pressure for high densities. The tower form, if provided with all amenities and if centrally located, may come next after, but some distance after, the single-family house as the preferred housing type in this country. Unhappily, the elevator apartment is also the most costly type to build, and the tower form is more costly than the slab. The tower provides better light and air and is a visually more handsome unit; the slab often has unpleasant proportions, and may block the view, create unpleasant shadows, or adjust clumsily to terrain. Internally, the standard central corridor prevents cross ventilation, and the system of exterior gallery access raises problems of unit privacy, danger to children, and exposure to weather.

Reference 30

The tall apartment has advantages of its own, besides its adaptability to high densities. Tenants are not responsible for maintaining buildings or grounds; they acquire some anonymity and social freedom; and they may be lifted up high enough to enjoy fine views. The buildings themselves provide dramatic accents at the urban scale: they can compose well with large spaces or relate to strong natural landscapes. Moreover, it is possible at these densities to secure special services such as catering, nurseries, convenience stores in the building, social rooms, or special recreation facilities.

Thus for some families without small children, the tall apartment may be a preferred living style and need not be confined to central areas. Its problems center about the access to ground, as well as the ground-level congestion of circulation, parking, unit storage, and recreation. It is usually preferable to furnish some outdoor sitting space close to the unit, by means of private balconies. Some outdoor play space can be provided on the roof, or even at intermediate levels, at a cost and with some danger. Stores and special facilities may be planned on upper floors, but it is usual to put these on the ground so that they can serve more than one building. Ground-floor dwelling units are at a disadvantage in tall buildings because of the activity about them and it may be necessary to screen them, or eliminate them entirely. It is fashionable to lift the entire building off the ground on stilts, but this is expensive and may cause unpleasant winds underneath, and it neglects many entrance, community, and storage functions which are logically located at ground level. With slab apartments, special care must be taken to prevent uncomfortable winds, shadows, or reflections of radiation or noise.

These are the prevalent American building types, but they by no means exhaust the possibilities. Other types remain to be developed, or to be tried out on a significant scale. One of the most important contributions that building designers can make is to refine the known types and to create new ones, since the bulk of residential building will follow such type patterns. Some of the new possibilities are:

1. *The courtyard house*, in which single-family units are packed closely together, side by side and back to back, and have their open space within their walls rather than outside of them. This derives from an old Mediterranean prototype, and allows the privacy, control, and directness of access of single-family houses to be provided at much higher densities.

2. *The combination of row housing with flats.* "Garden apartment" is now a euphemism for a two- or three-story walk-up, but the term originally applied to two-story row housing, of which some portion, particularly on the ends, was devoted to small flats, i.e., to single-story units stacked one above another. It is also possible, especially on sloping terrain, to place a two-story row house over a one-story flat. Or two two-story rows may be placed one above the other, to give the effect of a three-story walk-up in a four-story building. All these hybrids provide more variety of accommodation, and allow higher densities while still giving individual yards and direct access to many or all units.

3. *Doubled row houses*, with which high densities can be achieved where the units are not only side by side, but are also attached back to back. These have private yards and direct access, and are quite economical. Cross ventilation is difficult. The quatrefoil is a hybrid between this and the two-family type, in which four units are attached corner-to-corner, so that each has two open sides.

4. *Two-story units may be stacked vertically*, each having access to a common balcony which occurs every second floor. This is more economical than the usual apartment type, allows cross ventilation without loss of privacy, and gives some feeling of individuality to the unit. Many other variations may be rung upon the slab apartment, including the use of access balconies, skip-stop elevators with corridors every third floor and stairs internal to units, interlocking and through units, and so on. All these attempt to improve the privacy, economy, ventilation, or sense of individuality in the standard central-corridor slab.

5. *The small, standardized, prefabricated dwelling unit*, brought in and attached to the site in one piece, of which the trailer is now the outstanding example. This housing type raises many new problems and possibilities, which are touched upon at the end of this chapter.

The Space Between Buildings

The ground itself, in a residential area, must provide for more than the coverage of buildings. Typical uses that should be provided for include circulation (foot and vehicle), parking, play, sitting areas, gardening, laundry drying, outdoor work areas, disposal facilities, storage areas, utilities, landscape setting, and barriers to sight, sound, sun or wind. Concrete and grass are not ideal for all these purposes: an organized pattern of specialized surfaces is better, both visually and functionally.

These uses may be provided for individually, as in private yards, or communally, as in allotment gardens, public playgrounds, or group drying yards. Such group areas are an efficient means of providing room for these uses at higher densities.

When private yards are provided at the lower densities, then a space of about 40 by 40 feet is likely to be minimum if it is to be usable for sitting, play, and a few flowers. A simple "outdoor room," used only for sitting, might be as small as 20 by 20 feet. In any case, this space should be intimately related to the unit, with a suitable slope and good orientation. On steep ground, it may be necessary to employ open decks, or massive grading. It may be advantageous to vary the yard size with different units, giving better choice, or to use clusters of allotment gardens to allow for more extensive cultivation. Even in low apartment housing, a private yard for the ground floor units may often be arranged. At all but the lowest densities at least some part of the yard should be given visual privacy by a fence or hedges. These fences and hedges should be provided from the start.

Tall buildings at high density do not miraculously free the uncovered ground space. The requirements for use at the ground go up with the increase in density, and at the upper range of density the "free" ground area is likely to be largely paved and devoted to circulation, parking and intensively used play areas. Private balconies can to some extent substitute for the private yard.

The spacing between buildings has an important effect, not only on the ground left over for outdoor use, but also on the livability of the interior rooms. If structures are too close, especially if they surround a space, then noises may resonate within them. Every room should have adequate light and air: a substantial piece of sky should be visible through the windows from normal standing positions in the room. This will insure adequate daylighting and prevent claustrophobia. One way of defining a minimum standard is to say that from each window in the principal rooms the major part of the forward 60° cone of vision should be unobstructed by anything which is more than half as high above the sill as its distance from the window. This is automatically assured by spacing buildings at more than twice their height, but many other arrangements may be made by the use of towers and by the variation of orientation.

Even where this rule is observed, it may be unpleasant to look directly into facing windows which are so close as to destroy visual or acoustic privacy. Therefore it is well to avoid any layout in which one window faces another closer than 75 feet away. It is equally desirable, for visual relief, that at least some windows of a dwelling command a long, free view. All the views from principal rooms should be studied for their quality, particularly in relation to the time of day in which rooms are used, and it is preferable that the different rooms command a variety of views.

The orientation of buildings with respect to sun and wind is also important. It was once fashionable to seek an "ideal" orientation for a locality, and then to align all structures in that direction. The siting of buildings must still be studied carefully with respect to climate, but it is unusual to conclude, in ordinary circumstances in the temperate zone, that all buildings must be aligned in one direction. Properly spaced single- and two-family structures can usually adjust to many orientations. So can row houses, point towers, and gallery access slabs in which each dwelling has more than one open side. The interior plans in the latter types must often be varied to adapt to different orientations, however, and some alignments may be better than others. When the buildings are tall or long, shading and wind effects on the remainder of the site are significant, and the pattern and interspacing must be studied with this in mind.

The most difficult problem is the orientation of the tall, central-corridor slab, which not only has a serious external influence on wind and sun shadow, but whose dwelling units can have only one orientation. In the higher latitudes an east-west axis must be avoided to prevent sunless dwellings and ground areas in winter. At the same time, a north-south axis, while preferable, is not ideal, since it exposes some dwellings to the hot western sun of summer. In the tropics, such an alignment may be extremely uncomfortable. Thus the local climate, in regard to this particular type, may indicate a single "best" alignment, an alignment which in the Boston area would be a slab running north-northwest to south-southeast.

Storing the Car

The storage of the car is likely to be a major space consumer and a troublesome feature in housing areas. In wintry climates, most people prefer to use a garage which will protect the car from rain and snow and shield it from the lowest temperatures. A carport is only a substitute for this, and open parking, while workable, is third best.

Placement of the garage has never been satisfactorily solved except in low density single-family areas. The traditional location at the rear of the lot makes for a long driveway and a reduced private yard. A position near the street masks front entrances and destroys the street space while reducing safety for pedestrians. Placement in or under the units themselves is a good solution, but likely to be expensive, since the dwelling must then usually be made fireproof. Location alongside the dwelling, on the same building line, is often the best technique if there is sufficient space between units. Garages can be paired in this case. Arranging the garages in large compounds out of sight makes them inconvenient to the houses. Sometimes it is possible to group two to six garages together, between or behind the units, or in small courts, so that they are both convenient and not visually disruptive. At higher densities, any garages will most easily be concentrated in large multi-level structures, which are made part of the total composition of architectural masses. The cost of such structures makes it difficult to provide more than a fraction of the total parking need in this way. If garaging is placed underneath the apartments, it will be even more expensive.

In warmer climates, and in some cases in colder areas, the car will be stored in the open. And even where garages are provided, it is necessary to allow for the parking of additional visitors. It is now customary in this country to provide at least one and a half parking or garaging spaces per dwelling unit, and this ratio is rising. One car space per unit is considered a reasonable minimum in housing of moderately high density. At times, in central urban housing of very high density, the parking ratio may drop as low as one half space per unit, although this is certain to result in congestion.

Providing surface space for this parking at high densities begins to eat up all available ground, and yet garaging may be economically impossible. One compromise is to park one level of cars on a pavement which is a half-story below grade, and a second level on a light open deck above them.

At low densities, surface parking is a simple matter, being provided at the curb or in small one- or two-car parking stubs beside the unit. At moderate densities, it may become necessary to group cars in small off-street bays, since the alternative is to allow solid ranks of head-in parking at the curb, which is dangerous for children, disrupts traffic, and restricts the street view to an endless wall of cars. Solid curb parking can be ameliorated by occasional projections of the planting strip to break the line of cars and to provide a safe crossing for pedestrians. Curb parking must also be kept away from intersections. Even where cars are grouped into off-street parking lots, it is preferable to keep these lots no larger than six to ten spaces, since larger lots will be remote from the units and visually depressing. This rule is abandoned only when it must be, at the higher densities.

It is also possible to improve the look of small or medium-sized parking lots or stubs by dropping them a few feet below pedestrian grade, so that normal vision looks over the cars. This also makes it easier to screen the lots with planting or low walls. Trees may be planted throughout large parking lots, to provide shade and visual relief. But substantial open space must be allowed at the base of each tree, so that air and water may reach the roots.

Facility Standards

There is an extensive literature on desirable standards for nonresidential facilities in residential areas. The most important of these standards are summarized below. The usual warning must be made that these refer to the urban United States, to the present day, and to the completely average situation.

About two-thirds of an acre per thousand inhabitants is required for neighborhood convenience shopping. This is exclusive of community and central shopping, but includes such facilities as supermarkets, drugstores, laundries, beauty parlors, barbershops, shoe repair shops, and filling stations. This acreage provides for the stores, their access, and customer parking at a ratio of 2 square feet of parking for each square foot of selling space. It takes a market area of at least 4000 or 5000 people to support a center of any competitive strength and interest, and even this will be small. There is much to be said, however, for the provision of scattered small convenience stores within the housing area itself. The shopping center should preferably not be devoted to stores alone, but should also contain the offices, restaurants, clinics, libraries, meeting rooms, motels, and other common facilities that the community needs. It should be in close contact with the housing, highly accessible to it and to the outside world.

Another one and a quarter acres per thousand people will be required for playgrounds, serving the 6–12 age group. These should be within half a mile of their users, or preferably a quarter of a mile, with a minimum size of three acres. The elementary schools are commonly combined with them, and these schools demand approximately half an acre per thousand pupils for the building site, the setting, and access and expansion room. The minimum size for a combined elementary school and playground is five acres. If the school is separate from the playground, then additional play space must be added to the school site itself. Where there are no private yards, then additional play lots must be included in the plan, close to the dwellings, at a scale of about 50 square feet per child between two and six years of age. Walks, driveways, courts, or other hard surface areas are important locations for many kinds of play, which will otherwise occur in the street.

These standards do not provide for parks, whose standards are more variable, nor for schools of other types. They therefore represent only the bare minimum, local, formal requirements for the education and organized outdoor recreation of children up to twelve years old.

Schools and playgrounds, which are so vital and look so well on plan, may be nuisances for the immediately adjacent dwellings because of the noise and activity they generate. For this reason, and because of their large size, they do not compose easily in housing areas. It is advisable to site tall apartments near them, to turn low dwellings at right angles to their boundaries, to screen them, or to place them next to nonresidential uses. A pleasant but expensive solution is to bound play areas with roads, on which housing faces from across the street. Location next to shopping and other community facilities is of mutual benefit if the large play areas do not dilute the necessary concentration and accessibility of the center.

Recreation is a broad function, and its requirements are not met by the provision of standard play areas. Even for children recreation activities range widely, being both organized and unorganized, indoor and outdoor, daily and intermittent, local and distant. Sidewalks, for example, are a more important recreation facility than playgrounds, and should be designed with that use in mind. Particularly important for the child is the chance for adventure and for play of his own invention, in woods, swamps, back alleys, junk yards, and vacant lots. For the adult, the important recreation facilities may be special sports fields, commercial entertainment, access to natural scenery, city promenades, or the private garden. Many special recreational facilities may be provided locally: swimming pools, boat landings, parks, gardens, allotments, golf courses, skating rinks, walking and riding trails, picnic grounds. It is becoming more and more frequent for small housing developments in this country to provide some of these privately and locally, on a cooperative basis. Properly organized, they are very successful.

Many other types of community facilities are needed in relation to residential areas: libraries, recreation and meeting halls, clinics, fire and police stations, churches. While they must be provided for, and are significant in detailed plans, most of these do not make large demands on gross land area at the scale we are considering, except perhaps for churches, which will require sites of at least three-quarters of an acre. Churches and community centers generate substantial traffic and parking and should be sited at highly accessible points, where they will not disturb residential uses. With their heavy off-peak parking requirements, they are often successfully related to commercial parking lots. Fire stations, on the other hand, must be near several major roads, close to the center of the area served, and yet not at any point which is likely to jam, such as on a major intersection, or near a large parking lot.

These standards may not be directly applicable to a particular situation but are useful as first guides. They represent general opinion, rather than tested norms. Certain important questions, such as the relation of housing to work place, or to commercial recreation, or to more specialized facilities, are not covered at all.

References 14, 15, 16

One particular concept that must be dealt with here, though properly one of city planning, is the doctrine that houses should be grouped into "neighborhoods," units of from 2000 to 10,000 people, insulated from through traffic, bounded by green belts or other barriers, and self-contained as to all daily facilities except the workplace. This concept usually centers about the elementary school, and includes such devices as superblocks, neighborhood centers, and the separation of motor and foot traffic. The idea is based on a presumed unit of social organization, and has been applied and expanded in many different situations throughout the world.

Although the idea of neighborhood units developed in the urban United States, it does not seem to apply there. Most city dwellers are not organized socially in such units, and their life does not center about the elementary school. Nor would it be desirable if they were confined to such self-contained areas, with all the implications of local isolation and lack of choice. The attempt to fit all services into the same unit size is basically inefficient, a typical product of the professional weakness for solutions in which the components are neatly separated and grouped. In urban America, at least, the neighborhood unit seems to be a fiction.

It has been a convenient fiction, nevertheless. It contains some ideas of value and has attached itself to other ideas of value. The principal idea worth saving is that local facilities should be distributed so as to be easily accessible to all dwellings, and that when they are associated in common centers they are of special convenience and value. All functions need not occur at the same center, however, nor need their service areas necessarily coincide. The inhabitant of a residential area should have some choice as to his school or store or playground.

There need not be any neatly packaged areas, single-centered, of a magically ideal size. It will still be important to keep through traffic out of residential streets, and to see that small children do not have to cross such lines on their way to school. But these arteries need not be diverted to surround an inward-looking cell. Local shopping centers, for example, may best be placed along major streets, rather than inside the area those streets delimit. Similarly, the superblock is a useful device, and so is the separation of foot and motor traffic, where the flow becomes intense enough to justify it.

It may be desirable to group some dwellings so that the formation of true neighborhoods is encouraged, i.e., areas within which people are on friendly terms partly because they live close to one another. Such neighborhoods are much more likely to be of the scale of 10 to 40 families, rather than the 1500 families of the conventional unit. Physical arrangement may aid neighborhood formation, especially if the population is socially homogeneous, but factors such as class or personality are likely to be even more influential. Our urban areas are far too complex to be ordered by such a simple cellular device as the traditional neighborhood unit.

References 19, 20, 21

Residential Density

The housing type, its occupancy, its arrangement on the ground, and the facilities provided with it all result in a certain density of population. Density is associated with significant effects, and it is a useful concept in project planning. Unfortunately, the definitions of the various units of measurement are ambiguous and subject to manipulation. As a general guide to the site planner, the following densities are considered reasonable for the normal building types listed:

References 1 and 26, also page 30

Type of Unit	Floor Area Ratio	Families per Net Acre	Families per Neighborhood Acre
Single family	0.2	4–7	5
Two family	0.3	10–12	7.5
Row	0.5	16–19	11.5
Combined flats and row	0.75	25–30	15.5
3 story walkup	1.0	40–45	20
6 story elevator	1.4	65–75	27.5
13 story elevator	1.8	85–95	31

These are not magic figures, but represent reasonable densities in normal practice, using accepted standards for circulation, open space, and community facilities. Skilled design can move them upwards a little; abandonment of standards, especially for parking or play space, can move them upwards markedly. Any type can be built at lower densities than those given, although the justification for the type may be questioned when figures drop much lower, and it may be difficult to maintain community facilities and services at very low densities. Single-family houses are commonly built at significantly lower densities, going down to 1 or 2 families per net acre in some planned developments, or lower in the outer suburbs.

Although the floor area ratio and the families per acre are the common units of measure in this country, there are other units used in other countries, such as population or habitable rooms per acre or hectare. These measures may be more sensitive ones in cases of wide variation in family size.

With our present technology, it seems that in urbanized areas there is a broad range of density outside of which we should not go. The limits might perhaps be set at 1 and 120 families per net acre. Anything of lower density produces expensive, scattered development. It may be pleasant in itself but it leads to excessive city sprawl and a costly transport system. Community facilities become less accessible.

Areas of density higher than 120 families per acre can be built, but only with a loss of open space that results in sub-standard living conditions. These limits may change, however, as transportation and utility techniques develop, as living habits shift, or as we become able to build needed open spaces into buildings at upper levels. Twenty-story apartment developments are now being built, for example, at floor area ratios of 2.3 and net densities of 150 families per acre. These provide adequate light and air, but supply parking for only half the units and inadequate outdoor park and play space. In the American situation, they may be tolerable only for special families in special central locations. As an example of what is technically possible, new refugee housing has been built in Hong Kong at nearly 500 families per acre, and some slum areas exceed this by a good margin.

Even as it stands, 1 to 120 families per net acre is an extremely broad range, although it is significantly narrower when translated into neighborhood densities. It can perhaps be said that families with children between 2 and 10 years old should be housed at densities below 20 families per acre so that each family may have direct access to the ground. On the other hand, some recently married or childless couples, the aged, the unmarried, or those who have no sympathy for the joys and sorrows of house repair, may all prefer apartment living at higher densities.

Each building type has its own appropriate density, and the choice of density (if it is not fixed by city-wide considerations) should therefore depend upon the building type or types which are most appropriate to the situation. Some very general breakpoints, where the character of development is likely to shift, may be identified within the over-all range. At a density of about 12 families to the acre problems of noise control and privacy develop. Below this density it becomes difficult to provide maintenance of grounds or group facilities such as club rooms, nurseries, or laundries within very close range of the units. About 20 families to the acre seems to be near the point of maximum economy today, and above this density it becomes difficult to provide outdoor space, direct access from all units to the ground, easy surface parking, and external identification of units. At a density of about 45 families to the acre one is likely to lose most of the sense of visual intimacy or "human scale."

At 80 families to the acre, shortage of space for parking, for landscaping, and for recreation begins to develop. At the same time, certain "urban" characteristics have appeared which may be highly desirable: a wide variety of accessible activities and facilities, a wider range of human contact in a more formalized pattern. Above 100 families to the acre, the pressure for space becomes severe enough to affect the size of the dwelling units themselves and to make circulation congested. The upper ranges above 80 are suitable only for special family types living in central urban locations, who will accept limitations on their facilities for recreation and movement in return for central location. In sum, there is no one ideal, but the density variations have important implications.

A development need not be made up of one pure building type or density. Objectives often may best be met by some mixture, which will increase choice of dwelling for the resident and add visual interest. Care should be taken, however, to group similar building types in large enough areas to achieve their own typical environment. The transitions between types must be studied, both visually and functionally, as when tall apartments overlook the roofs and gardens of row houses. The composite net density of the mixed development is easily computed by adding the separate "pure" densities after they have been weighted by the percent of the net area allotted to each such density.

Page 117

The arrangement of individual buildings may first be studied at the level of a "module," or small group of structures considered as a repeatable unit (see Chapter 8). Residential buildings are in fact often repeated in a serial way, and their fundamental interrelations can be analyzed in the same way. Since it is the pattern of buildings and circulation that is most often primary to a site plan, rather than the lot pattern or the landscape pattern, modules of paths and building units are the most useful ones to know. The standard modules are only schematic, and new types can be created in the future. While worthy of study in the first stages of a site plan, they should not thereafter be applied by mechanical repetition. Despite these qualifications, a knowledge of the common modules of residential building grouping is a very useful one.

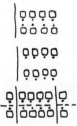

Most common, perhaps, is the street-front pattern, in which the building units, whether houses, rows, or apartment towers, are simply lined along both sides of the street. Access and orientation is easy, and there is little ambiguity in the plan. Although sometimes visually monotonous, the corridor space can be handled with strength, or at other times can be richly varied, by means of path alignment, building setback, and landscaping.

Principally for reasons of economy, a second general type has been developed in which rows of units are disposed end-on to the street. The street frontage per unit, a reliable index of site development cost, is thereby sharply reduced. Units are removed from the noise and danger of the street, but also removed from its convenience. Successive rows of units may face toward each other on common entrance pathways, or may turn their backs on each other to enjoy a common favorable orientation. Rows may run through from one street to the next, to form a continuous path system at right angles to the street system.

A third and highly favored module is the court arrangement, in which groups of units are faced inward on a common open space. This is done primarily for social and visual reasons: to promote neighborly relations and to provide pleasant enclosed spaces. Vehicular circulation may be allowed to enter the court, or may pass through it in some indirect fashion, as in the square, or may be excluded from it, as in the English "close."

The court with its circulation may shrink to the width

of a cul-de-sac. The internal space of the court or cul-de-sac may be open to the street, forming an inlet of the major street space, or the entrance may be narrowed or even formalized with a gateway, so as to produce an independent space. The land on the outside of the courts may be committed to public open space, to private yards, or to service access. In all these types, the land in the block interiors is relatively inexpensive, since it adds little to street frontage costs. Thus if raw land is cheap, reasonably large parks, gardens, or allotments may be provided there.

Reference 57

All these systems are usually economical of expensive street frontage except where loops are brought into the court, and are favorable (sometimes too favorable) to neighborly intercourse. They may complicate the street system, however, and make units difficult to locate for the stranger. Levels of the buildings must be watched carefully within the courts, which in general tend to look best on fairly flat ground, or when sloping uphill from the observer. Marked cross slopes tend to destroy the visual unity of the space, and a court or cul-de-sac lying downhill from the approach gives the terminal buildings a peculiar sense of inferiority and instability, in addition to raising practical problems of surface drainage and the flow of utilities.

A fourth general possibility is the cluster, in which a series of units, often uniformly oriented, is concentrated together and surrounded by some open space. The street may pass alongside, or penetrate within, this cluster. This module produces a strong visual effect of mass, which is the opposite of the spatial focus of the court type. Visual form can be given to an extensive area. Access may be complicated, but a sense of group unity can be achieved without forcing social intercourse. The most difficult problem is likely to be the interrelations between individual buildings, in terms of privacy and the use of adjacent land.

Still another method, if one rarely used, is to group the units in relation to each other and to the land, and then to introduce the road system according to an independent and rather irregular pattern of its own. In striking landscape, with lower densities or with tower structures set in much open space, this scheme may produce magnificent effects. But it easily lapses into disorder in unskillful hands, and is likely to be wasteful of space and of road length. It is difficult to accomplish at moderate to high densities.

A further possibility, of course, is the isolated point, where single family houses at very low densities, or single tall apartment buildings, are set by themselves in a landscape. Many of the site planning issues discussed above are then simply not raised, and orientation, economy, visual quality, and social effect are controlled by other things.

These diagrammatic modular layouts apply to all types of residential units, whether they be single family houses, rows, or slab or tower apartments. Differences in scale between these types will of course markedly change the visual effect.

Single- and two-family houses, in particular, are difficult to compose without an appearance of monotonous and restless repetition. This arises from their small scale with reference both to the size of a total development and to the scale of the car and its associated right of way. This is especially true of the modern one-story or one-and-a-half story small house, and is intensified where each building must be isolated and yet close to the next one. Where houses can be grouped across a footway or pedestrian space, the proportion of building height to open space can be made much more pleasant, and the ground surface can easily be designed to unify the whole. In the ordinary case, the reduction of street width and of the depth of front yard helps in a similar way.

References 3 and 22

Various techniques may be used to overcome these problems. Individual houses may be linked with screen walls, planting, garages, or porches. Garages themselves may be paired or grouped in compounds to improve their proportions. House spacing and setback may be varied to create visual groups, or to modulate the street space. Tall forest trees may be used to take over the role of space enclosure, contrasting with the low roofs of the houses, and providing a larger scale structure. The individual houses themselves may be made to relate visually by the use of similarities of roof slope and texture, of wall material, of the proportion of openings, or of the composition of horizontal lines such as eaves and sills. All these methods seek to form a larger visual unit than that of the individual dwelling so that the scale transition between the individual and the total project may be more easily accomplished. They need not entail absolute likeness between one unit and the next, although there is nothing wrong in principle with that kind of standardization, as long as visual groups are formed and a large-scale structure is composed out of them.

All the low-density house types, row housing included, suffer from problems of discontinuity at the ends and the crossing of roads. Spatial gaps are liable to appear just where strong enclosure is more desired, and there may be undesirable views of rear yards in enfilade. This may be avoided by screen walls, by making special house groups and setting them back so that closure is emphasized and a spatial punctuation made, or by the use of special corner units with reduced private yards or without them.

Row houses and low walk-up apartments may be used to enclose space in a much more continuous and flexible manner than single houses, although they still suffer from low height relative to street width. They may set back to form an emphatic space at an intersection or a curve, or they may be used in step or interlocking fashion both in plan and (on a slope) in vertical section. They may make sweeping curves, as in the crescents at Bath. They may form continuous enclosures, as in Hampstead Gardens, or be grouped *Reference 50* in looser rectangular layouts. The development of continuously modulated street spaces by the use of row housing is perhaps best illustrated in contemporary English work.

Slab apartment buildings can be sited in much the same way, if at a different scale. Large spatial enclosures and screens may be suggested which control substantial areas of ground and embrace the upper air. Towers may occur as punctuations, or be grouped in fluid lines or clusters. Greater spatial variety and freedom of siting can usually be achieved with these tall structures, because of their commanding scale, their independence of private yards, their lack of "front" or "back," and their flexibility of entrance location. They must be checked for their scale relative to the human being, for the pattern of access and service at their base, and for the effects of orientation.

The House Trailer

The design problems associated with small houses are intensified in the layout of trailer parks. Prefabrication of houses has long been heralded by experts, and has long been in travail. Now it has arrived, not from the quarter toward which everyone was looking, but via the house trailer industry. Trailers, or, more grandly, "mobile homes," have many substantial advantages for the small family: they are inexpensive; they can easily be bought and resold; the buyer knows exactly what he is getting for what price; they are compact and easy to maintain; fully-equipped, they can follow the family wherever it goes; they have the glamour of newness. These advantages are substantial enough so that trailers are used even when they must be transported by flat car or by large truck and will be fixed in place permanently or for a number of years. Families with children are using them despite their cramped interiors, and many recent models use ingenious schemes for expansion. Ten percent of the new housing produced is now of this mobile type, and the proportion will probably grow.

This poses the problem of the layout of the trailer park, or of any other development of small, standardized, prefabricated housing units. The solutions offered to date have been as dreary as those for the parking lot, and most people have concluded that the trailer is an up-to-date slum, to be banished utterly, or at least to be swept into some isolated corner. This is a typical human reaction to a new problem.

Trailer park layout does have many similarities to parking lot layout: the units are relatively mobile and sit lightly on the ground; they are of small scale and very numerous; they are made of shiny, hard, new materials. The units are even smaller than the normal single-family house, in relation to the car and the circulation room. They are almost the same size as the car itself. They are low, blocky, and typically very close together. Diminutive scale and mobility alone need not make difficulties: there are examples of handsome tent cities or nomad encampments. Part of the town of Oak Bluffs, on Martha's Vineyard, consists of tiny wooden houses packed closely together along pedestrian ways on what formerly were tenting grounds, and the effect is charming. The difficulty lies rather in the scale relations between street, housing unit, and the total project. It will certainly be necessary to group the trailers into large clusters, to make more use of landscaping for enclosure and rhythm, and probably to admit at last that the car itself is a necessary part of the scene, planning its location so that it will create space instead of destroying it. As the compact, standard unit, whether it be car or house, becomes a more and more frequent element in the landscape, in like measure the responsibility for organizing that landscape falls more and more heavily on the site planner.

The trailer or small prefab raises some difficult functional problems. Foremost among them is the need for privacy and for usable outdoor space which is generated by the very small size of the unit. This need is neglected in the standard trailer park, where the close rows of units look into one another's windows, and the only usable open space is a tiny patch of ground before the door. Privacy and usable open space require much more freedom and skill in arranging the units, and the use of planted screens, or perhaps of artificial, movable ones. The problem is compounded by the variety of models in one park with different interior plans and openings. The manufacturer is concerned with the product itself: no competent study has been made of the relation of such a unit to its exterior setting. Connected with this same compactness of the trailer unit is the increased importance of indoor and outdoor community facilities for recreation and social intercourse.

There are further functional problems: utilities must be connected or disconnected at will, and foundations must be removable and transportable, or able to serve many different types of units. These are primarily problems of product design, but they affect the layout of utilities and the design of the site. The common response to the need for a visual connection between the structure and the land has been the use of foundation planting to hide the clutter underneath and to make a pretense of a solidly rooted house. A more logical solution would express the new kind of connection in some elegant way.

Not only does the trailer sit lightly on the ground, but it has a shape and a skin that is new in the world. These shapes and textures are all too often ugly in themselves and must be improved. But even if well done, they would still contrast sharply with the forms of landscape and of traditional building. A connection between these contrasting forms has yet to be accomplished. One-to-one mixtures of the opposing elements are likely to be difficult: techniques of grouping, with the use of transitional elements or bold juxtapositions, promise more success. Undoubtedly, this sense of visual novelty and of clash with the existing landscape lies at the bottom of much of the adverse public reaction to the trailer. The designer who first fits a trailer park happily into its environment will be a hero.

A final crucial design question is that very sense of mobility which attracts many of the purchasers of trailers. Even when the unit may actually be fixed in place for a substantial time, there is still a sense of impermanence. Impermanence, real or fancied, raises many serious community problems of taxation, social relations, and service and participation that are beyond the scope of this text. In addition, the psychological and esthetic sense of impermanence, however pleasant to some, and perhaps in part to all of us, inhibits the sense of history and of place, and the emotional ties to objects or locations which develop with long association. It may retard the formation of friendships not based on family or occupation.

In this sense of impermanence the trailer park reflects the family mobility to be found in many American residential areas today, but here this mobility is more sharply expressed. It would be a mistake to react by make-believe: to camouflage the trailer as an ancient feature of the site. Many human societies have been nomadic, and yet their communities have been strong and their attachments to the land firm. The trailer park designer may be inclined to encourage neighborly association by his layout, or to use landscape elements which will express the permanence of the earth to which the units are momentarily attached, and which will serve as nuclei for a sense of history and place.

Chapter 10

Special Types of Site Planning

Shopping Centers

The location of a shopping center depends on analyses of market and accessibility. The market analysis considers the distribution of population, its buying power, the location of competing centers, the means of access to the site and their capacity, the time distances involved, and the customary routes of travel for other purposes. Centers are typically located along major arteries, and it is desirable to have more than one line of access. But a position at a major intersection or close to a freeway ramp may make access complicated, and a position along a highway already flowing full, and used primarily by fast through traffic, may discourage customers. Good visibility from the main lines of travel is desirable. The area to be developed should be level and fairly compact in shape, with no surrounding development that is ugly, competing, or of nuisance character. Area requirements vary, but a common feeling is that a regional shopping center requires at least 50 acres of ground. A common rule of thumb divides shopping centers into three types: the neighborhood center, dominated by a super market, containing about 40,000 square feet of selling area, and serving perhaps 10,000 people; the community center, featuring a variety or junior department store, having from 100,000 to 300,000 square feet, and serving 20,000 to 100,000

References 32 and 34

people; and the regional center, with one or two major department stores, and serving a large urban area. Such generalizations are only useful in first guesses, however, and must be developed by detailed analyses.

The composition of a center in regard to the types and sizes of stores can only be judged on completion of market and financial analyses, with the balance between kinds of tenants being quite significant. Large centers are now beginning to add other facilities in addition to retail stores, including theaters, offices, banks, post offices, and even hotels, clinics, and cultural facilities. In this way the shopping center begins to resemble the older central district, except for its isolation from the immediate surroundings, and the lack of residential facilities or of commercial activities using space of marginal quality. It is this local isolation, and this narrowness of function, that remain the most serious disadvantages of the new centers. When a shopping center is being planned by public agency as a part of a larger area, it is possible to correct some of these faults if we cease to ape the privately-built, self-contained center. Community facilities would then be introduced as a matter of policy, and shopping would be connected to surrounding residences and supporting service and commercial activity. Developers themselves will sometimes encourage the growth of adjacent motels, offices, and apartments.

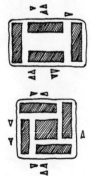

Shopping centers normally consist of one- or two-story structures, 100 to 200 feet deep, with basements. Individual stores within these large structures may run the full depth, or they may be as small as 40 feet deep, with a 20-foot frontage. Centers typically take one of several general forms. They may be arranged in the traditional pattern, as a strip along the street, or the strip may be bent into a "U" or "L" shape, set back from the artery it faces, with landscaping or, more likely, car parking occupying this forecourt. The stores may surround a hollow square, occupied with service entrances and surface or decked parking, while the stores front outward to pedestrians and streets. This is a compact type, suitable to central shopping, but there is liable to be insufficient space for parking. More commonly in this country the stores will be arranged in an inward-facing square, with parking and access on the outside, and a landscaped pedestrian court within. Usually this inner court is narrowed and lengthened to form a pedestrian shopping street, or "mall." Lastly, the stores may be clustered together compactly, with parking and access outside, and a web of pedestrian ways inside on which the stores front, so that some stores, particularly the major magnets, are completely within the pedestrian zone. These general forms may be further varied by using two levels instead of one, by allowing vehicles to penetrate the interior spaces, by making stores double-fronted, or by roofing over the pedestrian ways. Recent experiments are being made in high density areas with centers in which the stores are sandwiched, in one large structure, between layers of parking above and below.

The location of the various types of stores is critical. The basic principle of location is to expose store fronts to the maximum foot traffic, keeping this traffic in concentrated channels and at the same time well distributed over the center as a whole. Rather than allow the customer to enter his destination directly, and to leave it as quickly, paths are located to bring him past the remainder of the center.

Certain stores are considered to be primary attractions which draw customers to the center by their own power. Such are the department or junior department stores, large specialty and fashion stores, and, in smaller centers, variety stores and supermarkets. These activities not only draw people to the center itself, but can be located so as to pull buyers past other stores, and distribute traffic evenly. Other secondary attractions, such as banks, post offices, quality restaurants, clusters of apparel stores, and groups of service outlets (barber, beauty shop, shoe repair, cleaner), can also be used to cause people to move about the center. Other

FIGURE 33 *Stonestown Shopping Center, San Francisco, California. A typical new center with its central mall and large external parking lots. Note the added housing and office buildings on the periphery, and yet the lack of fit with the surroundings.*

stores are presumed to subsist from the distributed foot traffic so generated, while supporting the primary stores by the variety of goods and service they afford.

Normal practice in store location, therefore, is to put the primary attraction in the center, or as a pair of opposed magnets if there are two. Then the remaining secondary activities are distributed about the periphery to encourage balanced pedestrian flow throughout the area, the service outlets being put at the further margins or on a lower level. Other stores are grouped by similar types and prices of goods to facilitate comparison shopping: food, women's wear, family wear, housewares, and so on. Or, if certain activities stay open at night, such as theaters, restaurants, or drugstores, they will be kept together. Finally, goods principally bought on impulse, such as candy, pastry, gifts, tobacco, and cards, are sprinkled individually among the clusters. The details of pedestrian layout and the entrances are significant: the entrances from the parking lot and the bus terminal, the stairways, elevators, and escalators. The problem is similar in principle to the internal layout of a large department store.

The objective behind these arrangements is to maximize sales, and it is interesting to see that this objective sometimes coincides with the customer's objectives, when it facilitates comparison shopping, for example, and sometimes does not, as when it forces extended movement throughout the center to maximize impulse sales. Furthermore, since the objective is to maximize total rather than individual sales, neither does the pattern correspond to that of an unplanned business center. Where a shopping center is built by public agency for service rather than profit, some of these principles of location would be modified, emphasizing directness of access, grouping of similar stores, and clarity of form.

The interrelation between the circulation of cars, service trucks, and shoppers on foot is a standard problem. Generous parking, a short walking distance, easy service, and a pleasant pedestrian environment, are all desired, and are in some conflict. The traditional arrangement is to put service access on one side of the strip of stores and shopper parking on the other, with a pedestrian walk along the store fronts at the edge of the parking area. This is still a good technique for smaller centers, where shoppers move in and out quickly and the parking load is light. Store fronts and parking are visible from the first moment of entry, service is screened, and the shopper has the chance of parking close to the store he wants to patronize. But this system makes for an ugly view of parking lots from the main road, it prevents the development of a special pedestrian environment, and at larger sizes it becomes difficult to get parking within a reasonable distance of the stores.

A more recent system puts vehicular access on one side of the stores, and pedestrian shoppers on the other. Store service may occur along the "backs" of the stores, at the edge of customer parking, in screened-off bays, or even in basement tunnels. This pattern creates a pedestrian world along the fronts of stores, and, if the shops are arranged in a closed court, more parking spaces may be provided within a given distance of the shopping area. The view from the street on entering may be no more handsome, however, since the parking lot is still dominant. It may be even uglier, as the stores now turn their backs to the entrance side. A recurrent problem of this scheme is the entrance of shoppers into the inner court. How do they cross the service zone? How do they sense the quality of the inside area, or know where to go to reach the store they want? Some of these problems may be mitigated by putting the service underground, or screening it off; by arranging special entrances, or by giving the stores double frontage.

Provision for movement of shoppers still leaves much to be desired in regard to the visual experience of approach and departure, and the muscular experience of carrying of purchases back to the car. Subdivision of the parking area into smaller compartments, opening a view of the inner area to the outside, extension of fingers of landscaping or shopping into the parking area, mechanical devices for the carriage of packages out into the parking lots, and the integration of inner and outer circulation into one clear system, are all helpful.

It is also unfortunate that shopping centers are usually designed only for people arriving by private car. It is unnerving to walk into one from the outside, and they are rarely tied to any system of public transit. Like any highly specialized device, these centers may have a short life. Some centers are now providing bus terminals as an integral part of the design, and receiving substantial patronage from them. Location on a subway or railway line might also be possible.

Figure 34, page 160

Various rules are given for the amount of car parking to be provided. The simplest standards relate the number of parking spaces to the total area of selling space. Thus an older urban center, built at high density and drawing trade from transit passengers, may be contented with as little as

three parking spaces per 1000 feet of selling area. For most new centers, even those in urban locations which have transit access, five or six spaces are considered minimum. A regional shopping center, depending entirely on automobile trade drawn from a wide area and liable to sharp peak loads, may require seven, eight, or nine spaces per 1000 square feet. Such large centers may depend on the peak shopping of certain holidays such as Christmas and have overflow parking space for such times. These reserve areas, empty for much of the year, further complicate access to the center, and degrade its appearance.

The farthest parking spaces should be no more than 600 feet from the selling area, and these will be used only at peak sales periods. Everyday parking works best if placed within 300 feet of the selling area. It should be possible to have a general view of the lot on entrance and to move through it systematically while locating a parking space. Where land is cramped or costly, or even in order to minimize the car-to-store distance, split-level deck parking may be used. It may also be possible to depress the levels of parking lots by a few feet so as to reduce their visual dominance.

Since parking turnover is rapid, and customers are often entering cars with bulky packages, parking spaces should be generously sized, and as much as 400 square feet per car may be provided for lots, exclusive of main circulation, in preliminary layouts. For maneuvering, 45° parking is the easiest. Parking lots should be divided into areas of no more than 800 cars, each well lighted and identifiable. There should be walkways, and these walkways and the aisles should point toward the center. Drivers will want to get near

their point of first purchase, or to pick up heavy packages,
and thus there will be a considerable circulation within the
lots. Circulatory roads for this purpose may be put at the
outer edge or through the middle of the lots. If they occur
at the inner edge, they form a major barrier for the pedestrian to cross. Food markets require concentrated parking
near them, as well as pickup stations.

The circulatory system must take traffic off the public
roads into the lots and have sufficient length so that traffic
can slow down gradually and not back up onto the highway
itself. The peak loads are higher at exit than at entrance, and
at closing time employees and shoppers may leave within
one-half hour, although store closings can be staggered to
spread it out over a full hour. Exit and feeder roads must be

FIGURE 35 *The Merceria, Venice. Congested but dramatic, the display windows are at arm's reach.*

sized to take the impact of the expected peak emptying rate. Discharge of the lot onto more than one road is a distinct advantage.

In large centers trucks may circulate at basement level, to avoid conflict with cars. Separation of level is expensive, and it is desirable that store basements front along both sides of the truck route. This tends to locate the tunnel under an inner pedestrian mall, flanked by stores on both sides. Alternatively, service may be accomplished in special common bays behind the stores, the bays being screened off from shopping traffic.

Wherever it is located, service traffic should branch away from passenger traffic as far away from the center proper as may be possible. A shopping center may have one truck per day for every 4000 square feet of selling area, and more in the case of supermarkets. As much as 10 to 20 percent of the daily volume may accumulate at any one time. Generous storage areas, usually at basement level, are required to supplement the selling areas.

The designer of a shopping center usually has some scope for adornment, since the center is normally under unified control, the locational values created are concentrated and high, and there is a strong economic motive for display and a handsome environment. Special landscaping and paving; careful attention to outdoor furniture and other detail; the use of color, sculpture, fountains, and special displays; and the inclusion of facilities such as outdoor restaurants, kiosks, resting places, auditoriums, meeting rooms, exhibit space, libraries, and nurseries or play areas for children can often be justified. Signs may be carefully coordinated for harmony and legibility so that they also become ornamental. An orderly architectural framework for the individual store fronts may be created.

To strengthen visual identity from the highway the designer will use stacks, water towers, signs, flagpoles, and tall buildings for landmarks. The character of the skyline from the road, including the intrusion of roof structure, must be controlled. The intervening sea of parking is played down as much as possible.

The sequence of interior spaces may be carefully proportioned to give a sense of intimacy, contrast, and activity. Store fronts should not be too far apart. Their contents ought to be visible in detail on both sides of any pedestrian way, except where an open space is inserted which is itself to be the center of attention. On the other hand, depending

Figure 35, page 161

on the number of shoppers, spaces should not be so tight as to feel congested and oppressive. A pedestrian street 40 to 60 feet wide is likely to be about right. The shopping mall should not be so long as to discourage movement from one end to another, and in the larger centers it may be preferable to use "side streets" and other devices to keep the selling area compact. Two levels of stores and shopping streets have sometimes been used to bring the stores close together. This can be done on a split-level arrangement, to minimize vertical climb, and escalators may be used. But it is difficult to induce shoppers to change level except where they are forced to, and thus one level may be highly favored, and the other one "dead."

The plan should allow for future growth without disruption, but not by leaving gaps at the center. Primary stores, fixed in location, will probably grow vertically. Other stores will grow by addition at the periphery. Structures and utilities should be designed over-sized to allow for this expansion. Large-scale growth may be met more efficiently by building another center, rather than by continuous addition to the original unit. The development must be able to operate as a compact whole from the beginning, without depending on future additions. Similarly, each future stage must be a workable unit.

Industrial Estates

Like the regional shopping center, the organized industrial district is a new type of development. But in contrast, there has been little refinement of the technique of siting industrial uses. Yet industrial layouts affect the efficiency of the economic base, the daily environment of a substantial percentage of the population, and the appearance of the city as a whole.

Reference 35

Industrial districts require substantial areas of moderately flat and inexpensive land. The land should lie to the leeward of housing areas, and in such a position that the traffic it will generate will not disturb such areas. Districts range upward in size from 150 acres, with an average near 400 or 500 acres. Oversize districts may be difficult to relate to other uses, while districts which are too small may be uneconomical to serve efficiently. But there is no reason, from a planning viewpoint, why certain kinds of light industry may not be mixed even more intimately with other uses, given adequate controls.

Good access is the primary requirement for industrial areas, particularly for trucking and for workers coming by private car. Although most small and medium-sized industries today make little use of rail service, and many districts are now oriented only to highways, it is still desirable to locate a district on a rail line to preserve flexibility of service for future tenants. Districts are often far from public transportation, although bus lines may later be routed near them. The tendency of industry to become more and more dependent on a single means of access may in the end prove shortsighted.

Industrial districts are typically laid out with a gridiron of roads which enclose large blocks 1000 to 2000 feet long, and 500 to 1000 feet deep. If there is rail service, the tracks usually run through the mid-block, parallel to the long axis. Thus individual plots can have a street in front and a rail line behind. The plots should be from 200 to 500 feet deep. They are not at first marked off along the street: the frontage is assigned to individual tenants according to need at the time of sale or lease. Some general-purpose factory space may be erected before tenants are found, to provide for small enterprises and to act as "nurseries" for new and growing firms unable to plan for, or invest in, their own plant. Planning, financing, and maintenance or supply services may be extended to other tenants as well.

Most industries want to assure themselves of room for future growth and will buy plots substantially larger than presently needed. There are also large open land uses, such as heavy storage and car parking. Buildings are generally one-story high to allow easy horizontal movement of materials. Thus the floor area ratios tend to be low, ranging from 0.1 to 0.3, with 0.2 as a likely average. Density of employees per acre will also be low in these new industrial areas, ranging from 10 to 30 workers per acre. These are United States norms: in other situations where there is greater pressure on the land, as for example in England, or in central urban areas, floor area ratios may come closer to 0.5, and employee density to 60 workers per acre, while total estate size may lie in the 50 to 150 acre range.

Circulation is the key problem: industry is largely concerned with the assembly of goods and people, and the energy and time costs of this assembly is a significant portion of total cost. Thus the emphasis on high capacity access, flat land, and one-story plants.

Where rail spurs are provided, they should be given a

40-foot right-of-way, have a maximum grade of 1 or 2%,
and a curvature no greater than 400-foot radius. Spurs typically diverge at small angles. In the road system, lanes must
be of ample size, rights of way broad (up to 100 feet), and
docks and turns must accommodate the large tractor-trail- *Pages 182 and 183*
ers. It is desirable to separate truck circulation from the general circulation of passenger cars as much as possible within
the district.

Extensive parking space will be needed for workers'
cars. Considering some doubling up, it is perhaps enough to
allow one car space for every 1.2 workers, but some planners prefer the more generous figure of one space for each
worker. Since one shift arrives before another leaves, spaces
must unfortunately be adequate for two shifts of employees
at one time. The problem of exit congestion at shift time will
be serious, and the capacity of interchanges and exits must
be checked to see that they will permit this flow. A network
of secondary roads which permits quick dispersion of the
concentrated load is preferable to a single high-capacity
highway. Staggering of shift hours will also help. These peak
flows of workers' cars have become the principal conflict
between industrial and residential uses, in place of the traditional nuisances of noise, smoke, and dirt.

Since almost all drivers are destined for one particular
location in a plant, a location well known to them, parking
places may be more dispersed than in a shopping center, and

FIGURE 36 *A typical industrial estate: New England Industrial Center, Needham, Massachusetts. Low, bulky buildings in flat land on an irregular gridiron, visible from the expressway,
but disassociated from their surroundings.*

more closely related to the actual point of work. Day-long parkers can also be asked to walk further to their cars than short-term parkers. The maximum distance from car to plant may be nearer 1000 feet, rather than the maximum of 300 or 600 feet in a shopping center. Despite all this, internal circulation in the district should have a simple and understandable form so that traffic disperses quickly to its destination and visitors are not confused.

Clear visual identity for district exits and entrances is important, and can be accomplished through large-scale landscaping or vertical features. The ability to control or check movement at these gates may also be significant. Special loads are likely to be imposed on the utility system by factory operation, and the rules of thumb for residential areas are of little value here. Power, water, and sewage disposal of high capacity will probably be required.

As the daily environment for many people, these working areas tend to suffer from isolation. They are vast and sealed in; there are no independent local facilities to serve employees or to give some relief from the factory routine. To this end, it is possible to introduce such items as stores, restaurants, bars, parks, or places of recreation. It is not unusual now to provide group facilities useful to the industries themselves, such as banks, post offices, fire stations, and medical clinics. It may also be desirable to provide a small shopping and service center, with a bus or transit terminal, in conjunction with the industrial district. Extensive parks or recreation grounds, if provided, must be planned to resist the inevitable pressure for subsequent expansion.

Visually, the industrial district is difficult to deal with, even though the individual buildings may be competently designed and the customary cosmetic landscaping has been applied. The structures are typically dotted over a flat, empty landscape, dominated by parked cars. Asphalt and chain-link fencing are the predominant materials. The interesting industrial processes are generally invisible, and one new factory looks much like another. Only heavy industry now seems to retain the interest that comes from the visibility of its activities. The view from the bordering roads is important, both for its advertising and its scenic value, and the problem is not solved by the use of large signs, however attractive. Factories should not be allowed to back onto arteries or other areas from which they are visible. Perhaps it might be possible to develop the street frontages more intensively, whether by structures or planting; or to clarify and enclose the points of approach; or to make the buildings more expressive of the activities going on within them. Some of the landscaped areas might be developed for use, rather than being thought of as empty land to be made decent with grass. Architectural control, or at least design review, may be exercised over the plant buildings, and there might even be some attempt to group factories by type and mass to achieve certain visual effects. Storage and parking yards may be screened by planting or fencing. A general landscape structure and character may be introduced, although it must necessarily be broad and simple.

Institutions

Institutional land uses are extremely diverse in nature, and yet a few comments can be made about site planning for the larger groups: colleges, universities, hospitals, governmental units, and cultural centers. Such activities are normally long-lived as well as complex and extensive, and with this continuity it is possible to achieve environments of great richness and strong character. For the most part, the grounds of American institutions stand in sharp contrast to this possibility. It is astonishing how little the popular and romantic conception of a campus corresponds to its actual disarray.

Reference 33

Figures 37 and 38, page 169

Institutional site planning has several marked characteristics. The structural units are highly individual. Rather than a repeated series of factories, stores, or houses, there is a juxtaposition of classrooms, public meeting places, offices, libraries, clinics, residences, wards, laboratories, museums, ceremonial rooms, studies, and research areas: a collection of singularities. Each structure requires particular services and a particular situation, and must be studied by itself.

This diversity of use often makes it difficult to isolate basic objectives which bear on physical arrangement. Administrators may respond to queries with vague generalities, remaining convinced that there is no vital link between the site plan and their essential purposes other than the obvious requirements for shelter and access. Or they may hold a conflicting set of objectives for "flexibility" or for "balance." Yet the institutional case is par excellence the one in which long-term purpose and policy can be hammered out by those who are involved in its consequences, and where these policies can be applied most nicely to the planning of the physical shell. Therefore the planner is responsible for raising such issues as staff interaction, patient and student morale, flexibility, image, access, climate, cost, or community relations. He can often succeed in inflaming and informing the debate at the beginning by presenting physical alternatives which have direct and startling consequences for those policies.

Within the individual structures of the institution occurs a fluid and shifting set of activities, with many complex linkages throughout the institutional group. At present it is difficult to isolate more than a few of the most obvious of these links, but in the future the interconnections may be studied as a total system. For the present, the planner can make only a first approximation of the activity arrangement that will optimize such linkages for his given purpose. He is understandably prone to group activities along traditional lines, as by university department or medical specialty. Closer study may show that these standard patterns ignore sensitive spontaneous linkages, such as those between research workers in different fields. Careful analysis of linkage is likely to be quite important in institutional work.

Where the interconnections are many and overlapping, generalized time distances between all probable pairs of communicating activities become critical. Movement is typically on foot or in slow public vehicles such as elevators (or belt conveyors in the future?). Face-to-face interactions, spontaneous or planned, are important. When walking times exceed certain limits, the institution begins to operate in sectors, rather than as a unit. Students may be unable to move from class to class unless curricula are compartmented; staff will not meet those from other branches without special provisions for clubs or other meeting grounds.

The problem is an interrelated one of total size, of density, of the disposition of paths and foci, and of grain, or the relative size and specialization of units and how they are mixed together. A typical problem of grain in a university, for example, is the intermixture of departments or parts of departments. Another is whether all graduate-student housing should be in one place or several, separate from or integrated with other housing, in close contact with the teaching facilities or not. The size and density of the school, its purposes, and the rhythm of graduate student life will determine a unique solution.

Similar problems of access must be studied in relation to the world outside the institution. There will be activities to which it must be closely linked: clinics, private offices, shop-

FIGURE 37   *One of the rare examples of a serene and ordered American campus: the Lawn of the University of Virginia, designed by Thomas Jefferson.*

FIGURE 38   *A part of the University Circle area in Cleveland. This is the normal condition of an urban institution: a chaotic collection of buildings besieged by cars and with little room for growth and change.*

ping, restaurants, laboratories. It will require good general access to its supporting population of citizens, patients, or students. It will typically have to provide many types of entrance without chaos or interference for staff, visitors, clients, and suppliers. All of these are problems of multiform linkage, and in this the large institution is much like a city in miniature.

The links are not only complex but shift unpredictably. In a hospital, for example, a rapid connection between a single ward and a certain therapy unit may suddenly become important. Activities move in and out of a given building, expanding and contracting. Functions change in unforeseen ways. Long-term growth may be certain, but its rate is not easy to manage or predict. Therefore a high premium must be put on flexibility: on a physical shell that is easy to change or to add to, or on a good communication system which allows connections to be built up in any desired direction.

At the same time, most institutions of this kind have symbolic importance and will put strong emphasis on a visual setting which creates a certain mood, whether of awe or serenity or stimulus. The unity and expressiveness of the environment is essential. The designer has the problem of producing a strong over-all form and character which can also house complex functions and survive major change. He turns to the techniques of long-range site planning described *Page 107* in Chapter 7. Planned landscaping, lighting, and path systems may be of great help to him. He will tend toward monumental forms, and he will take advantage of the continuous control that is available. He will certainly recommend the establishment of a continuing planning staff.

The prediction of future growth and change, and its translation into future program requirements, is a normal part of the work. Immediate space demands are usually calculated by summing up the short-range needs of the various units of the institution and arranging them in a consistent priority order. Longer-range growth is more likely to be gauged by an estimate of the future growth of the base population: employees, patients, professionals, or students. To these estimates of population change are applied ratios of space per person for various kinds of facilities, such as libraries, classrooms, wards, clinics, laboratories, and offices. These ratios are derived from past experience and are modified by speculation as to future change. Typically, most institutions will underestimate future space demands and will look upon the next imminent building program as the last for all time. The planner must consciously overcorrect for this habit of mind.

Future requirements for land area may then be computed from the floor space requirements by fixing a set of desired structural densities, or floor area ratios. These will of course vary widely from institution to institution. A college of open plan may stay below a ratio of 0.5 or even 0.3, while an urban university may go up to 1.0, and a large city hospital on expensive land, and needing close contact between its working parts, may aim for a ratio as high as 2.5. In large hospitals, except where dealing with chronic or convalescent cases, the high-rise structure may be preferable simply because of the reduction of time distances between activities. The general pattern of structural density is an important feature of any institutional plan, since it will tend to determine site acquisition, service load, linkage between parts, future flexibility, and general visual character. There will be a continuous struggle to retain open space, whether for visual amenity, recreation, or future growth.

Parking is a problem for institutions as for any activity, but it is likely to be more difficult because of the conflict of the large parking lot with the symbolic meaning of the institution. Most professional and many nonprofessional staff

Ed Nano

FIGURE 39 *The campus becomes a parking lot: Case Institute of Technology, Cleveland.*

now drive to work; so do visitors, and even most students if they can. In order to preserve a quiet campus, the institution may have to take extreme measures, such as severe administrative regulation, underground garages, or distant fringe parking served by shuttle. In the institutional case it may be possible to impose a longer walking distance from car to destination. On the other hand, there are likely to be key personnel — doctors, professors, or research directors — on whose quality the institution depends, and who will use all their power to secure convenient parking for themselves regardless of the cost to the whole institution. Thus the institutional parking solution is likely to differentiate between users and require a full-fledged control system. Controls favoring small cars, or cars carrying more than one person, may also be employed. Parking charges may be used to defray part of the cost of the garages.

The long life and inner vitality of institutions has another consequence: the problem of their relation to surrounding areas. These areas are in time likely to change or degenerate in ways damaging to the institution, or to become completely unrelated to it in function. The question then arises whether the institutional area must be isolated from its general surroundings, or whether it can somehow be linked to them in a harmonious way. A typical decision to be made is whether the personnel of the institution should be housed within the institutional area itself, or in the community at large. The provision of housing for students and young staff is always a difficult issue because of its cost, its social effect, and its implications for the site plan. In its turn, the traffic and transient population that a large institution attracts may be just as damaging to its surroundings.

The technique of institutional planning is just developing. In theory, long-range controls and high purpose should produce the finest examples of site planning. That they do not indicates our inadequate grasp of the problem.

Urban Renewal

Urban renewal is the systematic rebuilding and rehabilitation of the city environment by a combination of public and private agency. A discussion of the total process lies far beyond the scope of this book, but a significant amount of site planning will be required as an integral part of this great task. Site planning in the renewal process is a small but critical corner of the city building domain.

Renewal design is fractionated, rather like subdivision design, if not so seriously. A general site plan, fixing use, density, circulation, public facilities, and building mass, is prepared by the public agency that will acquire and transmit the site. Other public or private developers then carry out this plan for their own purposes: public or private housing, shops, factories, offices, highways, transit lines. These developers may have been in close liaison with the original planners, or may have arrived only lately. In either case, the original agency has the problem of anticipating the developer's requirements, of judging how detailed its plan should be, and of devising controls that will carry out its intent and still allow flexibility to meet the unforeseen. The developing agency, on its side, must prepare a detailed plan in the spirit of the original one, and yet know when to attempt a breakout, whether because of a new idea or a new situation.

Ideally, both groups try to penetrate each other's territory, the developer helping to shape the original program, and the planning agency preparing an illustrative, detailed site plan. From this detailed plan the necessary controls can be extracted, controls that may be ironclad at certain critical points, and quite general elsewhere. Nevertheless, the separation in the planning operation, made necessary by the need for competitive bidding or administrative partitioning, is a chasm not yet easily bridged. The problems of co-ordination too often push us into using a single giant developer, squeezing out mixed uses or the small-scale tenant, regardless of functional or esthetic disadvantages.

In urban renewal the site planner is working over ground occupied by many human and physical assets, all entangled in the great urban spider web. These conditions demand a sympathy for city life and for the way in which it develops. Designers who perform brilliantly on clear and relatively self-contained sites will often raise havoc in urban renewal areas, as many of our visually isolated and visually inhuman redevelopment projects will mutely testify.

Reference 17

Part of the difficulty is that a typical renewal area is studded at random with structures that still have economic and social utility. The impulse of a designer trained to create order and pattern is to sweep them aside, or, if their retention is forced upon him, to seal them off like lumps of undigested foreign matter. But not only do these structures have economic utility, they are often esthetically valuable. They can provide variety and contrast to newer structures and preserve continuity with the urban past. Many human associations will have gathered about them, and they may accommodate activities which are economically marginal but socially useful. Key buildings or groups of buildings are often worth saving. Their retention need not be viewed as an episode in the epic struggle between the heavenly powers of Art and the satanic powers of Commerce. The issue can be resolved by a sympathetic inquiry into the actual human value of the existing buildings, and by a patient search for an order that will embrace the new and the old together.

This search for an embracing order is made more difficult by the requirement that rebuilding be done piecemeal and by stages, as older buildings and activities become obsolete and as the community acquires the power to carry out the plan. A formal order is unlikely to be successful; a flexible and multiform pattern must be employed. In all these characteristics, of course, site planning for renewal approaches the city-planning field on which it borders.

Retention of existing structures will most often be paralleled by the retention of some existing activities. These will also appear to be haphazardly distributed, but will usually reveal a hidden social or economic ordering. Once again, there will be weighty arguments against eviction of these uses, and esthetically they can provide much of the vitality and meaning that we associate with urban life. It is more important to make these activities and their interconnections visible and to find continuities of scale or pattern between them, than it is to suppress or conceal their apparent disorder.

The urban renewal designer resigns himself to the sad or glorious fact that his fabric will be inhabited by a whole sucession of activities. It is not his task to find a permanent shell within which they may all be confined, but rather to suggest a general principle of physical order to which the successive activities may attach themselves, and from which they may grow and elaborate. Thus an open space system or a circulation system may be a more important site-planning contribution than would be a pattern of building shapes.

Renewal sites merge into their settings. Their structures are part of a larger group, their streets run into neighboring streets, their activities are part of a city-wide network. Most redevelopment plans unhappily deny these connections; new projects focus inwards, turn their parking lots outwards, emphasize their distinctiveness. Designers and inhabitants call their developments "islands." Unfortunately, these design habits are reinforced by the administrative procedures which divide the renewal process into "projects" with sharp boundary lines. We cannot deal here with the question of form at the city scale, and lacking some public directive as to general city form, the site planner cannot contribute directly to an order at this comprehensive level. But he can at least make sure of the local fit of his design; he can concern himself with issues of approach or outward view, with boundaries and the tendency of human activities to overrun them, with harmonies of scale or form between site and setting.

When these points have been set down, it appears that they are only elaborations of the more general themes that have appeared in these pages. Yet they are so commonly neglected that it seems necessary to point out their special application to the problem of site planning for urban renewal.

Chapter **11**

The Design of Streets
and Ways

The Street Cross Section

Vehicular ways are laid out with a cross section which remains fixed for substantial distances. This cross section is usually located by the center line of the pavement. The principal features of the most common cross section are shown on the sketch below, but not drawn to scale. Many cross sections are possible, each with distinct technical and visual implications:

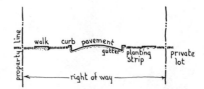

The pavement itself is usually crowned at the center for drainage, the cross sectional slope being ⅛ inch per foot from crown to edge for concrete pavements, ¼ inch per foot for bituminous surfaces, and ½ inch per foot for earth and gravel roads. A six-inch curb and gutter is used on major streets, while a roll curb may be used in rural areas, or on minor streets where residential densities are low. Even a simple turf or gravel shoulder, flanked by a shallow ditch about three feet wide and probably sodded, may be employed at very low densities. In residential work, the use of a ditch requires a culvert under every driveway and at each intersection. This may be more expensive than a roll curb or other device which uses the street as the drainage channel. The curb also prevents the breakdown of the pavement edge.

The pavement may be concrete, bituminous macadam, gravel, stabilized soil, or simply a graded and drained earth surface, depending on traffic. Its width is computed by summing up the number of traffic and parking lanes required.

Parking lanes, if provided, should be eight feet wide for parallel parking, or 16 feet wide for angled or perpendicular parking. Each traffic lane should be nine to ten feet wide on minor roads, and up to 12 feet wide on highways. The minimum vertical clearance is now 14 feet, to allow for the passage of trucks with high loads. A practical minimum pavement width for minor residential streets with light parking is one parking lane plus two traffic lanes, or 26 feet. If parking will never occur, this minimum may drop to 20 feet for a two-way minor road. On a one-way street with parking on only one side, the pavement may be 18 feet. Such a street might be used as a short loop, or as a marginal access road alongside a major thoroughfare.

The purpose of the planting strip is to separate the walk from the street for convenience and safety, to allow room for utilities and street fixtures above and below ground, to provide for piling of snow, and to permit the planting of street trees. It should be a minimum of seven feet wide if it contains trees, or four feet wide for grass alone. If paved, and used only for utilities, it may be reduced to two feet. In commercial areas it is sometimes eliminated, and poles and hydrants are placed in the widened sidewalk. In any case, street poles should be set in two feet from the curb, for safety. On important roads, the opposing traffic lanes may be separated by another planting strip, for reasons of safety, the channelizing of intersection maneuvers, the management of steep cross slopes, or for visual amenity.

Sidewalks should have a minimum width of four feet, although where they lead directly to single-dwelling entrances they may be only two-and-a-half feet wide, with a widening at the door. Collector walks handling large numbers of pedestrians must be six to eight feet wide. Walks, like street pavements, should be crowned, or have a two percent cross slope. Walkways are normally and rather monotonously made of concrete or of asphalt, but gravel, brick, and stone may also be used, or the concrete may be textured, colored, or laid in patterns. Walks may occur on only one side of the street in low-density residential areas. While the major walk system may be designed to be independent of the road system, there must be a walk on at least one side of all streets, except very short local streets or service drives, or roads in rural or semi-rural areas with no substantial fronting development. People persist in walking along or in the street, even in defiance of the designer. Walks are useful for children's play, and quite necessary where snow is frequent. In high density areas, they cannot be skimped, but must be wide enough to accommodate all the movement and social activity that will take place upon them.

The property line is set only a nominal distance outside the walk, unless public planting is desired beyond this edge. Street trees are perhaps best planted at this point, or in private front lots, rather than in the planting strip. This avoids the interference of branches with overhead poles, lights, and wires.

The right-of-way is the total public strip of land within which there is public control and common right of passage, and within which all pavements and utility lines are located if possible. Its width depends on the features included within it. The minimum is commonly given as 50 feet, but this can actually be reduced on minor streets to as little as 35 feet. This makes for a more economical and flexible plan, particularly in rough ground, and may improve the visual scale. Where the future traffic load is uncertain, it may be necessary to use a wider right of way, while beginning with a relatively narrow pavement. At the other extreme, a major freeway may require a right-of-way which is 400 feet wide.

Horizontal Alignment

Road alignment is generally referred to the pavement centerline, which is marked off in 100-foot "stations" for reference, beginning at some arbitrary end of the system. A separate numbering system is used for each single continuous line. All significant points, such as the intersections of one centerline with another, or the beginning and ending of horizontal and vertical curves, are located by reference to this numbering system.

Centerlines are made up of two kinds of elements used alternately: straight lines, called "tangents," and portions of circular curves, to which the connecting straight lines are tangent. If two curves are directly joined without an inter-

See below

vening straight line, both are made tangent to the same imaginary line at their junction. Tangents and circular curves are used for ease of layout, and so that curves, once entered, can be negotiated with one setting of the steering wheel. On major roads, the joint between tangent and circular curve may be softened by a "spiral" curve, which is one whose radius begins by being infinitely long (i.e., it is a straight line), and then progressively decreases until it reaches the radius of the circular curve which it is introducing. These spiral curves of transition are rarely used on minor roads, and will not be treated further here.

The circular curve has the following elements:

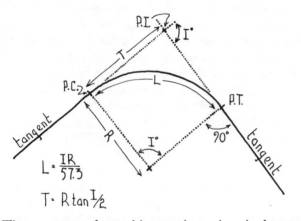

$$L = \frac{IR}{57.3}$$

$$T = R \tan \tfrac{I}{2}$$

The curvature of a road is sometimes given in degrees, a one-degree curve being one whose length is 100 feet for each one percent of internal angle, while a two-degree curve has the same length for two percent of angle, and so on. If curves are designed in whole degrees, then their staking out by the surveyor is somewhat facilitated. Conversion may be made by the formula:

$$R = \frac{5730}{D},$$

where R is the radius in feet, and D the degree of the curve. We will use the curve radius in the discussion below. The rules and standards which follow are based on the characteristics of today's automobile, and will change with it.

It is preferable to avoid two curves in the same direction, separated by a tangent of less than 200 feet ("brokenback curves"). They look awkward and are awkward to drive. Similarly, avoid two sharp curves in opposite directions, separated by a tangent of less than 100 feet. Gentle reverse curves may be directly joined without a tangent,

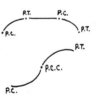

See table, page 191

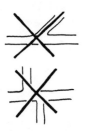

Reference 43

See table, page 191

however. Two curves of the same direction, but of differing radius, which are directly joined together ("compound curves") are avoided where possible but are occasionally necessary. The minimum allowable radius of a curve depends on design speed, or the speed which will be set as the maximum safe speed which can be maintained continuously on that piece of road.

On residential streets, tangents may be joined without an intervening curve where the angle of intersection is less than 15°. This may also be done at much sharper turns, where it is obvious to the driver that he must slow or stop before negotiating the turn, as at a street corner.

Street intersections should be within 20° of the perpendicular for 100 feet each way from the intersection. Intersections of acute angle are difficult to negotiate, and dangerously limit visibility for some approaches. Direct crossings, or crossings which are offset by at least 150 feet, are preferable to slight offsets, which frustrate the cross traffic, and disturb flow on the line that is being crossed. On minor roads, where the complications to cross flow are not of importance, the "T" intersection, sufficiently offset from the next junction, may be preferable to the straight cross for reasons of safety, or for closure of the visual space. Intersections with an arterial road, or major street, should be no closer than 800 feet apart, to prevent disruption to the major flow. On freeways, intersections will be limited to one-mile or one-half mile intervals. The curb at corners should have a radius of 12 feet for minor streets, or 50 feet at intersections with major streets, to allow easy turns.

Minimum forward sight distance must be maintained at all points on the line, to give drivers ample time to react to dangers appearing in the road. It can be scaled from the plans, taking account of buildings, hills, landscaping, and other blocks to vision. The minimum value depends on the design speed. A driver 75 feet from an intersection should see the entire intersection, plus 75 feet of the intersecting street on each side.

The maximum depth of a loop drive is usually given as 700 feet, and that of a cul-de-sac as 400 feet. The maximum allowable block length is 1600 feet. All of these refer to the same reasoning: as block, loop, and cul-de-sac lengths increase, general circulation becomes more indirect, service deliveries longer, and emergency access more liable to misdirection. These rules are commonly held standards of "reasonableness." They are not agreed to by all site planners. Obviously, they would not apply where through circulation is already blocked for other reasons, as on a narrow peninsula, ridge, or pocket of land.

A minimum turn-around at the end of a cul-de-sac should have a 40 foot outside radius free of parking, so that vehicles such as fire engines can negotiate it. This requirement demands a large area of ground and paving, and may defeat the purposes of small culs-de-sac. A T-shaped terminus or shunt may sometimes be provided for backing turns on very short dead ends. The wings of the shunt should be at least a car's length deep on each side, exclusive of the width of the street, and at least 12 feet wide if no parking is allowed. The inside curb should have a 20-foot radius. As long as these turning requirements are provided for, free of obstacles, a small short residential cul-de-sac need not adhere rigidly to these shapes. A more freely formed parking and arrival court may be quite desirable. Dead-end streets, furthermore, must be designed so that they do not form drainage pockets.

Individual driveways should be eight feet wide, the curb at the entrance being rounded off with a radius of three to five feet. Driveway entrances should be at least 50 feet from any street intersection to prevent confusion with movements there. Separate driveways and entrance walks should be provided for each dwelling unit, unless they are made common to large number of units. Walks and drives which jointly serve two or three units are potential sources of friction in regard to maintenance.

The maximum distance from the street to the door of a dwelling unit is often given as 150 feet for carrying convenience, and perhaps should be 100 feet. For similar reasons, there should not be a steep grade between house door and street. This street-to-door distance standard is also in dispute: some would restrict it to 50 feet; others would relax it to 300. It has an important effect on cost and on design freedom. It depends on the way of life: in America, both by preference and by necessity, this maximum distance is shrinking. In countries where much walking is customary, the distance could be substantially longer.

Houses should be located so that car headlights will not shine into ground floor windows, and so that there will be no danger of being struck by cars out of control. This often argues against axial positions at sharp curves or "T" intersections, especially at the foot of slopes.

Parking may be provided in various ways: on the street (which is convenient but expensive, and disturbing to moving traffic), in small parking bays, in large parking lots (which is cheapest, but may be inconvenient or unsightly), or underground or in ramp structures or garages (the most expensive of all).

Parking lots can be laid out if the following dimensions for the modern juggernaut are kept in mind: each stall should be 19 feet long and eight feet wide if attendants park cars, and 8½ by 20 feet if drivers park their own cars, or even nine feet wide to give a sense of ample room. If front bumpers cannot overhang the curb, then stall lengths may have to be increased by several feet. Stalls may be parallel, perpendicular, or at 30°, 45°, or 60° angles to the moving lane. Aisle widths range from 12 feet for one-way lanes serving 30° and 45° parking to 22 feet for two-way lanes serving perpendicular parking. For efficiency, there should be stalls on each side of each moving lane. Herringbone dividers placed between the inner ends of angle stalls will save some further space. Dividers and curbs may hamper snow removal and the future rearrangements of the lot, however. Most efficient patterns are the perpendicular stall layout, and the 45° angle with herringbone dividers. Least efficient is 30° angle parking. As a rough guide, over-all space requirements of large and efficient lots run from 250 square feet per car for attendant-parked lots in which cars are stored three or four deep, to 400 square feet per car for generous self-parking. The maximum allowable slope in any direction is five percent and the minimum one percent.

The circulation within large lots should be continuous, with dispersed exits and a minimum of turns. Lot entrances should be at least 12 to 14 feet wide, if one-way. Thought should be given to the movement of pedestrians to and from the cars. One solution is to provide a raised and planted strip between the ranks of vehicles. Tree planting will improve the climate and look of a parking lot, but requires substantial space for root feeding. Lots may be screened with walls or planting, or sunken a few feet to allow vision over them. In residential work, for the sake of convenience, visual scale, and individual control over the car, it is preferable not to allow parking in groups of over six to ten cars. Even in large lots serving commercial areas, it is preferable to keep the cars within 600 feet of their destinations, unless special transport is provided.

Large tractor-trailer trucks are about 50 feet by eight feet. They require a minimum outside turning radius of 60 feet, and a vertical clearance of 14 feet. Curb radii at corners must be 30 to 40 feet where such trucks are common.

Loading docks for trucks should be 10 to 12 feet wide per truck, set at truck-bed height — about four feet off the pavement — and arranged so that when backing, the trailer swings clear of the driver's line of vision. A 50-foot parking and maneuvering apron is needed in front of the dock. A general rule is that the floor area of a loading dock should be about twice the floor area of the beds of all the trucks that could be brought up to the dock at one time: this allows room for unloading and temporary stacking.

Capacity and Intersections

The capacity of a road depends on the characteristics of the road — width, surface, alignment, conditions at the edge — and of the traffic — vehicle type, speed, control, driver skill. The theoretical capacity of one lane of traffic is 2000 cars per hour where this flow is completely steady, uninterrupted, and at optimum speed and spacing. It might be approximated by a highly organized convoy moving on an ideal pavement. In practice, a multi-lane freeway may carry up to 1500 or even 1800 cars per hour per lane, while a congested street with frequent side friction due to cars parking and entering may carry only 200 to 300 cars per hour on the outside lane. A local residential street will carry about 400 to 500 cars per hour per lane. Four lanes in one direction seems to be the widest road which one can drive on without permanent loss of sanity.

Reference 42

When traffic flow is heavy, the critical limit to capacity is the intersection. Even where total volume through an intersection is as low as 500 cars per hour in all directions, up to 50 percent of the approaching cars may have to stop before going through or turning. Such an intersection, or any one handling higher loads, will require some treatment. The simplest is a stop sign on the secondary street. From there, the designer may go to traffic signals, channelization, or grade separation. The design and analysis of high capacity roads and intersections is a matter for traffic engineers, but some mention of it must be made to give the site planner a sense of the problems involved.

These intersection treatments are all devices for avoiding the elementary conflicting maneuvers, for moderating their difficulty, or for separating them in time or space. These elementary maneuvers are those of merging, diverging, and crossing, and their danger is proportional to the relative speed of the approaching vehicles. For example, the relative speed of two cars in head-on collision is the sum of their individual speeds, while that of two vehicles going equally fast, and merging at a slight angle, is almost zero. A direct two-way intersection has 32 elementary conflicting maneuvers.

Traffic signals, by alternately stopping some entering movements, reduce the number of conflicts. They may be warranted when intersection volumes rise above 750 vehicles per hour, with at least one-quarter of the flow on the minor street. They may have a simple two-phase cycle, which alternately passes the traffic of one street and then the other, with a yellow interval between each change. Or they may be more elaborate, with three, four, or even more phases, to allow unhindered left turns, or the entrance of more than four streams of traffic. Total cycles are usually from 35 to 50 seconds long, and each intervening yellow interval is about three seconds. The capacity of such a controlled intersection can be computed roughly by assuming that 1000 vehicles can move through each lane per hour of total green time, i.e., excluding for each movement all its red and yellow periods. This is a high figure attainable under optimum conditions, and does not allow for the effects of heavy trucks, left turn or pedestrian conflicts, or any stopping or parking at the crossing. Practical figures are closer to 300 to 600 vehicles per lane per hour of green.

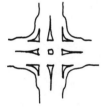

Channelization, which is the separating of lanes by the use of islands and medians, does not reduce the number of conflicts, but separates them in space and time so that only one conflict need be dealt with at one moment by the driver. It allows drivers to wait for a favorable chance to conduct one maneuver, without preventing other drivers from conducting other maneuvers. It also makes all maneuvers either merging-diverging at low relative speeds, or direct right-angled crossings, where the driver has better visibility and the conflict is of shorter duration than in angled crossings. Channelization is often used in conjunction with traffic signals at major intersections. Even on minor intersections, islands may be used to improve safety, or to provide room for planting, or to allow an easier adjustment to steep cross slopes.

The rotary is a device to convert all crossings into merge and diverge sequences, that is, into weaving operations, which are safer because of their low relative speed. Since only one lane can weave at a time, the total capacity of a rotary is never more than can be gained with one lane of crossing flow around the circle. They are useful where total intersection flow is of the order of 500 to 3000 vehicles per hour, depending on the predominance of through and left-turn movements. At this order of flow, they are particularly useful where more than four roads converge. The length allowed for weaving is critical for capacity: at 25 miles per hour, a 100-foot weaving section may carry only half the normal single lane capacity, and 400 feet be required to give full single-lane flow. At higher speeds, 800 feet may be required for full capacity, and 300 feet for half capacity. Minimum weaving lengths are usually set at about 200 or 250 feet. The width of the rotary pavement should at least equal the number of entering lanes on the largest incoming street, plus one lane. The rotary keeps traffic moving smoothly where flows do not exceed these single lane levels, and where the circle can be made large enough to give adequate weaving length. But where rotaries are small, or flows exceed the capacity of the single weaving lane, traffic is liable to "freeze." Rotaries are difficult for pedestrians to cross, except via bridges or tunnels.

Grade separations are expensive, space-demanding, confusing to the driver, and inflexible in regard to future change. They should be used only where necessary, that is when a channelized intersection with signals cannot carry the load. A grade separation is often considered necessary when the flow on the major channel is over 3000 vehicles per hour.

One of the most common types of grade separated interchange is the cloverleaf, with its indirect left turns. Cloverleafs may be full or partial, depending on whether all possible turns are allowed. They take much space and are confusing in form but the public is by now somewhat adjusted to them. Capacity is high, except in regard to the left turn, where no more than a single lane can diverge, and speed is slow around the tight reverse turn.

If left-turn volumes are high, then a direct left-turn interchange may have to be used, which requires a complex and expensive structure. More than one lane can be pulled off, and in a direction which makes more sense to the driver. Left-turning ramps may be provided for all left turns, or only for particular ones.

Where only one channel is a major one, it is common to use a bridged rotary, or a diamond intersection, in which conflicts are allowed on the secondary road, but not on the major one. The diamond type, in particular, is saving of space in tight urban situations.

Many special types of grade separation are in use or can be developed. However complicated, they can be analyzed by tracing out each possible through or turning movement, and by checking the capacity of each such part of the intersection with expected flows in that direction. Special types for particular problems can best be developed by the use of movement diagrams, beginning with the expected pattern of heavy flows. Such diagrams explain the conflicts resulting from alternate patterns. Colors can be used to separate levels diagrammatically and to indicate the bridging required, which is indicative of the total cost.

Rough scale drawings can then be used to check whether the intersection would be workable and to indicate the space required. The requirements that are most critical for the size and feasibility of a separated intersection are the maximum ramp grades, the minimum ramp radii, and the minimum lengths of acceleration and deceleration lanes. Maximum ramp grades are usually given as follows:

	percent
up ramps	4–6
up ramps, high volume	3–4
down ramps	8

Minimum ramp radii are the same as those for any traffic pavement, and depend on design speed (see the table on page 191). Design speeds of 20–30 miles per hour are usually used on such ramps. The required length of acceleration and deceleration lanes, including the entering taper, depends on the relative speed of traffic on the main road and on the ramp being entered or left. Given a ramp designed for 20 miles per hour, then the required total lengths are:

	Design speed of highway, miles per hour		
	40	*50*	*60*
Length of deceleration lane & taper, ft.	250	350	400
Length of acceleration lane & taper, ft.	250	450	700

The capacity of such complex intersections must be analyzed part by part: the through lanes, the turning lanes, and so on. Limits to capacity are likely to be met at the acceleration lanes, where turning traffic is merging back into through traffic. Here, if the maneuver is smoothly designed with an adequately long acceleration lane, total flow in the merging line may come up to 80 percent of full single lane capacity. Where major flows are coming together, it may be possible to bring in two lanes instead of one, although merging cannot be effected for a long distance. In the extreme case, it is also possible to allow two, three, or even more separate lanes to merge or diverge simultaneously into or from an equal number of through lanes, by using separate on or off ramps for each set of lanes. Obviously, this is a complex, expensive solution.

Vertical Alignment

The vertical alignment of the centerline of a road is also made up of straight tangents — constant upgrades or downgrades — with vertical curves at the junctions. These vertical curves are parabolic rather than circular. Parabolic curves are used because they are easy to set out in the field, while still making a smooth transition between the intersecting grades. The grades of the tangents are expressed in percent, or the feet of rise or fall per 100 feet of horizontal run. By convention, grades are given as positive percentages when uphill in the direction of increasing numbers in the stationing, negative when downhill.

See below

The minimum grade of tangents is 0.5 percent so that water will drain off the road surface, or 0.25 percent if construction is done with particular care. The maximum grade of streets depends on design speed. Maximum grades should not be long sustained. A passenger car cannot stay in high gear if the grade is continuously above seven percent, while a large truck must shift down on sustained grades of over three percent. Maximum grades are somewhat flexible, depending on winter conditions and on local habits due to prevailing terrain. Where icing is severe, anything over 10 percent may be too steep, while in San Francisco regulations may allow grades up to 15 percent on minor streets. A 17 percent sustained grade is the most that a large truck can climb in lowest gear.

The maximum grade of sidewalks should be ten percent or less, if icing is frequent. Short ramps at breaks in grade may go up to 15 percent, however. If steps are used, there must be at least three risers, so that they will be noticed, and accidental falls avoided. The steps should be designed to prevent by-passing. A useful rule for proportioning exterior steps is that the height of two risers added to the width of the tread should equal 27 inches. Riser height may vary between 6½ inches as a maximum and 3 inches as a minimum.

The parabolic vertical curve has the following elements:

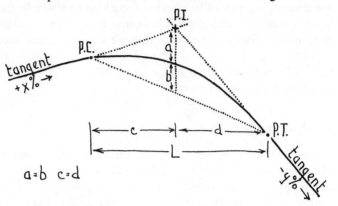

The parabolic curve drops below the original tangent line in proportion to the square of its distance from the point of curvature, but it can easily be laid out graphically with sufficient accuracy for residential work. Choose the length L, locate the PC and PT so that they are equidistant horizontally from the PI, draw the chord, then locate the intermediate point of the parabolic curve, which is halfway, vertically, between the chord and the PI. PC, intermediate point, and PT are three points on the required parabola, which can then be drawn with a French curve.

To prevent a jolt for the driver, vertical curves are required between tangents of the road centerline wherever the algebraic difference in grade between the tangents is two percent or more. (In the diagram above, the algebraic difference between the intersecting tangents would be X% $-(-Y\%)$, or $X + Y\%$). Where the algebraic difference between tangents is over nine percent, the long low modern cars will strike the road surface in passing the break in grade. Therefore, vertical curves must be used in driveways at this or higher differences, of sufficient length to prevent such a grade change within a six-foot length. A curve which is one foot long for each one percent of algebraic difference in grade will accomplish this.

The required length of vertical curves in a street is controlled by "roadability" — the avoidance of an unpleasant jolt in the vehicle making the grade transition caused by an excessive acceleration or deceleration of vertical velocity —

and by the need to maintain adequate sight distance. For roadability, the minimum length of the curve for each one percent of algebraic difference in grade of tangents depends on design speed (see the table on page 191). If, for example, the gradients in the diagram were +5% and −8%, and the design speed were thirty miles per hour, then the required curve length would be: 20 (15 + 8) = 260 ft.

Minimum forward sight distance must be maintained throughout the vertical as well as the horizontal alignment. This is computed as being vision from a point four feet above the road to a point four inches above the road, and may be scaled from the profiles. Sight distance may sometimes require longer vertical curves at summits than needed for roadability. In sag curves the resulting length of headlight beam must also be checked to see that it is equal to minimum sight distance.

See below

Profiles should be flattened at street intersections, so that halted vehicles need not hang on their brakes, and can start easily. There should be a "platform" of not over four percent grade, extending at least 40 feet each way from the intersection. This often causes difficulty where many cross streets intersect a street on a steep gradient, and must sometimes be sacrificed.

The vertical alignment of a road is developed on a profile drawing, which shows the cross section of the existing ground at the road centerline as if this sinuous vertical section were flattened out onto a single plane. The profile is usually drawn to a vertical scale ten times the horizontal scale, which is also the scale of the horizontal layout. Each profile drawing describes one successive run of station points. The new road profile is developed by a series of trial sets of tangents, as described in Chapter 8, and then vertical curves of the required length are constructed between these tangents.

Once developed, the proposed elevations of the centerlines can be returned to the base map for the grading plan in the form of tick marks showing where the new contour will cross these centerlines. And since the road cross section is known in advance, these new contours may be drawn as far as the tops of curbs as a step preliminary to making the grading plan itself.

It is easiest to contour the street surface as follows: knowing the fall from crown of road to gutter, the contour will cross the gutter at a point proportionally as far uphill toward the next contour above as the fall from crown

to gutter is to the contour interval. Thus, if the crown is six inches above the gutter, and the contour interval is two feet, then a contour will cross the gutter one-quarter of the way uphill between where that contour crosses the centerline and where the next contour above crosses the centerline. This may easily be approximated by eye. Similarly, the point at which this contour will cross the top of curb will be proportionately as far downhill of the gutter crossing, as the height of the curb is to the contour interval. Once tick marks have located the crossings of centerline, gutter, and top of curb, then a smooth curve can be drawn freehand between them, a curve which will have the slope of the road cross section in exaggerated form. Thus a road that rises, falls steeply into a sag, and rises again more gently, would if contoured have the appearance shown below:

Chapter 8 discusses the subsequent preparation of the grading plan. In doing so, it becomes clear that the road profile is a major determinant of the grading plan, and must often be modified to allow the development of a good scheme. Modifications are often necessary even if the vertical alignment is in itself consistent, up to standard, and seems to minimize cut and fill along the centerline.

The Alignment as a Related Whole

The horizontal and vertical alignments must be considered together, since what is being planned is actually the locus of a single centerline in three-dimensional space. The perspective view of that centerline in space is an important visual feature of the landscape: it is markedly different from the road alignment as it appears in plan. Small unexplained dips and bumps look awkward, especially when they are made clearly visible, as on a long flat curve, or a long grade seen from the side. Some shapes give the sense of discontinuity or twisting: a dip just before a curve, a dip in the tangent within a broken back curve, a horizontal curve that begins in a dip, or a bridge that is skewed to the road or whose deck does not fit smoothly into the vertical alignment. There are handsome combinations, for example, when vertical and horizontal curves coincide, or when the approach alignment is arranged to display a fine bridge from the side.

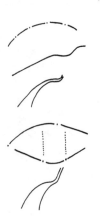

A good rule is to avoid the partial overlapping of horizontal and vertical curves, or to make sure that no visual distortion results from the overlap. It is often useful to construct a simple string or cardboard model of the road centerline and thus to analyze its appearance directly.

For reasons of safety, sharp horizontal curves should be avoided on high hills, in deep cuts, or at the foot of steep grades. The change in direction on a reverse curve should not occur when going over a summit. Where a horizontal curve occurs on a grade of over five percent, the maximum allowable percent of grade on the curve should be reduced by one-half percent for each 50 feet that the curve radius is less than 500 feet.

The following table indicates the variations in alignment standards according to design speed. An appropriate design speed for minor residential streets is 25 miles per hour. Major streets would be designed for 35 or 40 miles per hour, and highways for 50 or 60. Maximum grades at the slowest speeds may be increased somewhat where ice and snow is infrequent, but these grades should not be continuous for long stretches.

ALIGNMENT STANDARDS IN RELATION TO DESIGN SPEED

Design speed, in m.p.h.	Minimum radius of horizontal curves in feet	Maximum % of grade	Min. forward sight distance, in feet	Min. length of vertical curve for each 1% change of grade, in feet
20	100	12	150	10
30	250	10	200	20
40	450	8	275	35
50	750	7	350	70
60	1100	5	475	150
70	1600	4	600	200

Chapter 12

Utility Systems

Storm Drainage

The storm drainage system takes off the flow of surface water. It is a substitute for natural surface drainage, and it may be unnecessary in low density development of less than one or two families per acre. It need not be a united system, but can discharge into local streams, lakes, and gullies wherever it will not cause flooding or increase pollution. If natural water bodies or drainage lines are not available, it is possible to discharge into settling pits or overflow basins. These are made in pervious soil, and must be big enough to hold water from the worst storm, temporarily. They can also be used to economize on the length of main needed to reach a stream or public sewer, but they render useless a substantial piece of ground and are not very handsome.

Since pipe sizes required are often large, the storm drainage system is an expensive one, and every effort is made to minimize or eliminate it. The pipes of large diameter at the bottom of runs may cause difficulties in the grading plan by tending to "ride up" out of the ground while they maintain sufficient elevation to reach their destination, or as they must flatten out to prevent scour inside the pipe. Nevertheless, since the roofs and paved surfaces of residential developments usually interfere with existing surface flow and increase run-off, some artificial drainage is usually required to prevent flooding during storms. The storm system is today normally kept separate from the sanitary drainage to minimize the volume that must be treated in sewage disposal and to prevent backing-up of sanitary wastes.

The storm system is made up of a drainage surface, a set of open gutters and ditches, and probably a series of underground pipes, usually made of vitrified clay and laid straight to line and grade, connected by manholes and fed by inlets. Large sewers, over 42 inches in diameter, are usually made of concrete instead of clay. When the pipes become large enough for a man to enter for inspection or cleaning, they can be gently curved in horizontal alignment. It is now becoming accepted practice in some localities for all sizes of sewer lines to be laid in regular horizontal curves, as long as the radius is not less than 100 feet and the vertical grade is constant. Particularly where streets are curving, this technique minimizes sewer length and the number of manholes, and allows the sewer to remain in a standard location with reference to the street and other utilities. The smaller lines cannot then be inspected visually, and flow is somewhat slower, but modern cleaning machinery can easily be sent through such curves. Small curved sewers may not be permitted by local ordinance, however.

Manholes — man-sized circular pits — are used to enter the lines or to look down their length. They are placed at the upper end of lines, and at every change in horizontal or vertical direction or curvature. They should also be placed no more than 300 to 500 feet apart to permit the use of cleaning apparatus. An economical design will minimize their number, in addition to minimizing the length of line.

Surface water first flows in a film across the ground, and it is kept spread out as long as possible. The aim is to keep surface water moving, but not so fast as to cause erosion. Allowable slopes therefore depend on the volume of water expected, the surface finish, and the amount of damage that can be done by local flooding. Planted areas and broad paved areas should have a minimum grade of one percent, although open land far from structures, where occasional ponding can be permitted, may slope as little as 0.5 percent. Streets and other paved surfaces that are laid to exact elevations may also have a minimum of 0.5 percent, or even 0.25 percent. Land should slope away from all buildings for ten feet with a minimum grade of two percent. Drainage swales and ditches require a similar minimum of two percent, and a maximum gradient of ten percent, or of five percent if the area drained is over half an acre. Lawns and grass banks can have a maximum slope of 25 percent, while unmowed planted banks can slope up to 50 percent, or perhaps to 60 percent in firm, undisturbed soil. Expensive cribbing or retaining walls are needed to hold steeper slopes.

The ground should be sloped so that there is positive drainage throughout, even if there is also an underground system, since that underground system may at times be clogged. Undrained sinks and sag curves should be avoided. The designer must be aware of the quantity and velocity of flow entering his site from the outside, and how it may change in the future. On the other hand, if he wants to avoid claims for damages, he contrives to let surface water leave his own property only along the drainage courses previously existing, and never in greater amount than before.

As surface drainage builds up in volume but before it begins to concentrate naturally and to form gullies, it is concentrated artificially and put under control in artificial channels. It is picked up by the walks or in grass ditches, and delivered into the street gutter or ditches. Where swales or ditches drain more than one lot of land, they must be open to common maintenance, and easements are required.

In the street gutter, the storm water can be allowed to flow for some distance before being taken up by the underground drains or discharged off the property. This gutter flow should not be allowed to run across a street or walk, and thus it must normally be picked up at least once on each block, at the lowest corner, or be carried under the cross road in a culvert. Usually the gutter will have sufficient capacity to carry the flow from one block, although it is desirable not to allow water to run more than 800 to 1000 feet before reaching the sewers. If necessary, the capacity of a gutter to carry any given flow can be tested by the Manning formula. No substantial gutter flow should have to turn a sharp corner or meet a sudden obstacle, such as a protruding driveway apron. If it does, a heavy flow may jump out of the gutter and cause erosion and flooding.

See page 199 for the Manning formula

The flow from gutters and ditches, if not previously turned into a natural drainage course, is finally caught by inlets placed in the gutter or face of the curb, usually at street intersections or at low points in streets or grounds. They have a grating to hold back large debris, and are connected by short branch lines to the main drain, preferably at a manhole. Catch basins are sometimes inserted between the inlet and sewer, or in the manhole, to trap grit and trash. But since these basins may become nuisances, and require frequent cleaning, they are used only when much grit may enter, from sandy soil or earth roads, and where slopes are flat and velocities low.

Sewer lines must be covered deeply enough to prevent breakage and freezing (four feet in the latitude of New England), while if they are buried more than 20 feet deep, the excavation work will become costly. Lines must have a minimum slope so that the velocity of flow allows self-cleaning. The slope required to achieve this velocity depends on pipe size and quantity of flow, but may be taken as 0.3 percent minimum in preliminary trials before size and quantity has been determined. In later calculations, this minimum velocity is taken as two feet per second when flowing full, which will provide for sufficient speed when the sewer flows only partially full. On the other hand, the slope must not give velocities over ten feet per second, which begins to cause scouring of the pipe. This may demand large pipes and flat slopes in the lower ends of lines as quantities build up.

Changes in slope may be made only at manholes. Manholes may be of the drop type, where the upper line enters above the lower receiving one. Otherwise, the ends of two connecting lines are laid so that the tops (not the bottoms!) of the pipes are at the same level. However, the vertical position of pipes is traditionally specified by giving the elevation of the invert, or the lowest point on the internal surface. A pipe is never allowed to discharge into one smaller than itself.

The storm sewer system is initially laid out in plan, locating the first inlets as far down the slopes as possible, within the limit for flow in the open gutter. The pattern of converging sewers is then arranged so that there is a minimum length of line, and a minimum number of manholes, which are nevertheless placed to be close to all necessary inlets, and to allow straight runs within the right-of-way between their locations. Since repair and cleaning is usually done at the manhole rather than in between, the manholes must be in the right-of-way, but the sewer lines themselves may occasionally run through easements separate from the right-of-way. Preliminary profiles of the top of the sewer pipe are then plotted on the street profiles, with the pipe as close to ground surface as possible within the limits stated for cover and minimum slope. Since the system must meet the outfall sewer, settling basin, or stream at the right elevation, it is easier to draw this preliminary profile upward from the discharge point. Finally, pipe size must be computed by the site planner or his engineer, in order to estimate cost, check velocities in the pipe, and avoid excessive depth of cut. Technical problems of the storm drainage system will sometimes require modification of the general site plan. In laying out the system and computing pipe size, the designer must take account of other areas draining into the area under study, and of the possibility that more intensive development may increase future drainage.

See below

Occasionally a development has to be laid out on a completely flat or swampy site, which raises problems for all the utilities. Storm drainage can sometimes be handled by keeping the crown of the road dead level, but letting the gutters alternately rise and fall, so that they will discharge into a series of inlets along their length. Here the water falls into the underground system or, if there is no outlet for an underground system, the water runs off through ditches to overflow basins, where the water is ponded until it seeps into the ground. The land surface is graded so that house sites and paths are above the pond levels, and thus the critical parts of the site are protected from flooding. Such retention basins, or even the street itself, may be used for temporary ponding, so that pipe sizes lower down can be more efficiently sized.

Computation of Pipe Size

As a preliminary to finding required pipe size, pipe flows are computed by the general formula $Q = CIA$, in which Q is the quantity of runoff in cubic feet per second, I is the intensity of rainfall in inches per hour, A is the drainage area in acres, and C is the coefficient of runoff. Q is in cubic feet per second, even though I is in inches per hour and A in acres, simply because the unit "inch-acres per hour" happens by chance to be very closely equivalent to cubic feet per second. A complete exposition of the assumptions and techniques involved in the use of this formula is unnecessary for general site planning work, since an engineer experienced in these utility systems would be required to detail them. It is worthwhile, however, to understand the basic method, since the formula is one used in all drainage work, including river systems and open land drainage, and also because it is useful to be able to make a rough check of quantities, pipe sizes, and slopes in the lower ends of storm drainage lines. In any case, 12 inches is the minimum diameter for a storm sewer that drains a street, and 10 inches for one that drains a yard area. These minima are set to prevent stoppage by trash.

The coefficient of runoff C, the fraction of total rainfall which runs off on the surface, may vary from almost 1 on waterproof surfaces — or even over 1, where warm rain falls on ice or snow — to as low as 0.01, in dense old woods with spongy soil. The coefficient for any area may be estimated from the following approximate values:

	C
Roofs, asphalt and concrete pavements, other waterproof surfaces	0.9
Macadam, compacted earth and gravel, without plant growth	0.7
Lawns, parks	0.3
Unpaved yards and lots, overgrown	0.2
Woods	0.1–0.2

Or it may more quickly be estimated for composite areas from the following:

	C
Development at 10 families/acre	0.3–0.5
Development at 40 families/acre	0.5–0.7
Dense urban areas	0.7–0.9

Variations within the ranges depend on the perviousness of the soil, its plant or artificial cover, and the steepness of slopes.

The intensity of rainfall, I, depends on the general climatic region in which the site is located, and also on the chosen "year of storm," or the frequency with which a storm of that intensity is likely to occur: a "five-year storm" being of a kind likely to occur once every five years, a "twenty-year storm" being an unusually heavy one occurring once every twenty years on the average, and so on. A low year of storm may be chosen as the basis of calculation for scattered, low-value development where an occasional overload of the system is not critical. A higher year of storm would be used for a dense, high-value area where even infrequent flooding might be serious, and the resulting system would be an expensive one, rarely used to capacity. Ten-year, or even five-year storm frequencies may be used for residential development, and twenty-year frequencies for shopping centers.

The intensity of rainfall during a storm also varies from moment to moment. It is usually assumed from general experience that intensity is at its peak at the beginning of the storm and then slacks off gradually. Thus the intensity of rainfall occurring at any moment depends on the climatic region, the chosen storm frequency, and the elapsed time since the storm began. This rate is estimated from the past rainfall experience of the area, as summarized in local hydrologic or weather data. For most of New England and the Middle Atlantic and North Central states, the rate of rainfall may be estimated as:

$$\text{Five-year storm: } I = \frac{131}{t + 19}$$

$$\text{Ten-year storm: } I = \frac{170}{t + 23}$$

$$\text{Twenty-five-year storm: } I = \frac{230}{t + 30}$$

where I is the momentary intensity in inches per hour, and t is the time in minutes since the beginning of the storm. A note at the end of this chapter suggests a procedure for constructing rainfall formulas if they are not available.

Page 210

The value of t used in a calculation for pipe size is the time required for the crest of maximum flow to reach the point on the line in question. At the top of the line, this time is simply inlet time, or the interval needed for the largest volume of water to reach the inlet from its tributary area. Inlet times vary from 3 to 20 minutes, and may be taken to be ten minutes in suburban residential development. In general, inlet times vary directly with the distance to the farthest point of the drainage area, and inversely as the coefficient of runoff and the square root of average slope. The time used for calculating intensity, and thus the quantities entering inlets, at the next manhole down is the original inlet time plus the time required for the initial crest of flow to run from the first to the second manhole. The crest is then carried down from manhole to manhole, the time gradually lengthening, and the intensity therefore gradually slackening.

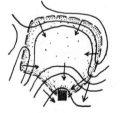

The area, A, which is expressed in acres, is simply the total area drained by each set of inlets. Knowing that surface water flows perpendicularly to the contours, the "divides" between inlet drainage areas can be drawn, and the size of each area computed by planimeter. Off-site as well as on-site drainage areas must be included in the analysis.

The total flow leaving each manhole to enter the next section of pipe is therefore the sum of the rate of flow of the crest arriving from any line above, plus the rate entering at that moment at the manhole's own inlets. The latter quantity is computed from $Q = CIA$, using the values of C, I, and A proper to this set of inlets.

Knowing this rate of flow leaving the manhole and, from the preliminary profile, the slope of the next run of sewer pipe, the required size of this next section may be computed from the formula:

$$D = \left[\frac{Q}{10\pi S^{\frac{1}{2}}} \right]^{\frac{3}{8}}$$

where Q is the rate in cubic feet per second, S is the slope written as a decimal, and D is the inside diameter of the required pipe in feet.

Since D will come out as a fractional number, the pipe chosen for use should be the next standard size larger. Standard sizes of sewer pipe increase by two-inch increments from 4 to 12 inches, and thence by three-inch increments to 36 inches. Pipe should never be oversize, since resulting velocities at light loads may be too small.

(This formula for pipe size is derived from the Manning formula for flow in open channels:

$$V = \frac{1.5}{n} R^{\frac{1}{2}} S^{\frac{2}{3}}$$

where V is the velocity of flow in feet per second, S is the slope written as a decimal, R is the hydraulic radius, and n is the coefficient of roughness of the inner surface of pipe or channel. This coefficient varies as follows:

	n
smooth pipe	.01
concrete	.013
brick or vitrified clay	.015
smooth earth	.02–.035
rough channel, overgrown	.03–.05

The hydraulic radius, R, is equal to the cross sectional area of the flowing water, divided by the length of that part of the cross sectional perimeter of the channel which is in contact with the flow.

This formula may be employed for pipes at atmospheric pressure, and for ditches, open channels, gutters, and streams. But it should not be used where velocity is over ten feet per second, or where the hydraulic radius is greater than ten feet. It is used to calculate velocity, given the slope, the hydraulic radius resulting from the depth of flow in the channel, and the co-efficient of roughness due to the type of channel. The rate of flow is then the product of this velocity times the cross sectional area of the flowing water.

This general formula has been simplified in our text above by assuming the use of vitrified clay pipe ($n = 0.015$), circular and flowing full, since the purpose is to find the smallest pipe that will carry the expected flow. In this case R is equal to one-fourth the inside diameter of the pipe, and the cross section of flow equals $\frac{\pi D^2}{4}$.)

After pipe size has been calculated, the velocity of flow must be checked. The velocity when the pipe flows full will simply be the rate of flow divided by the cross sectional area of the pipe in square feet, using the fractional pipe diameter derived from the formula. If the resulting velocity in the pipe is outside the preferred range of between two and ten feet per second, then the slope of the pipe must be readjusted. Then the required pipe size and velocity must be recomputed, and the process repeated until a satisfactory combination is found.

With the velocity and the length of pipe known, the time for the crest to move down the line can be computed and added to the previous t to give the new t to be used in computing rainfall intensity at the next inlets. Thus the entire system can be sized, running down each branch from tip to junction.

At a junction where several branches converge, take the crest which arrives last and readjust the flows entering from other branches to what they would be contributing at the time the last crest strikes. This can be approximated by multiplying each branch's crest of flow by the ratio of the rainfall intensity at the moment of arrival of the last crest to the rainfall intensity at the arrival of the branch's crest. The flow of the last crest to arrive is added to the simultaneous flow of each other branch, and the process goes on down from the junction until the end is reached.

Normally, this system would be computed and designed by an engineer specialist, but it is useful for the site planner to understand the computation and its implications, and to see how it can be applied to all kinds of drainage work and flow in open channels. With this knowledge, a designer can always check a particular ditch or gutter or run of pipe that may be critical for size or slope. Since trouble often appears at the bottom of a run, the last pipe is often worth a check.

The quantity of flow at the end, or at any point in the line, can be approximated without going through the step-by-step process described above. Use an over-all C, and an A that covers the entire site drained by every inlet up to and including the last one upstream. Take an I which is an average between that expected at the top inlet ($t =$ inlet time), and the I that would be expected at the last inlet just upstream, if the crest had moved down from the longest branch at some reasonable constant rate, say four feet per second. The quantity Q computed from these values of C, I, and A can then be tried out at the slope tentatively given for the line in question.*

A short length of pipe, inserted under a road or other barrier to carry storm water or a small brook, is called a culvert. It is in effect a fragmentary storm drainage system. Normally culverts are circular in cross section, and made of concrete or corrugated metal. They should be straight, should cross the road approximately at right angles, and should use the line of the old channel if possible. But in any case they should cross the road at the first opportunity, and not allow water to course along the uphill side of the road, which causes erosion.

Where possible, they are laid at the slope of the old channel, but with a maximum grade of eight to ten percent and a minimum grade of one-half percent. The gradient just below the outlet must be at least as steep as the slope just above the inlet, to prevent silting. Inlets and outlets require wingwalls and aprons to prevent erosion. The culvert should be covered with four to seven feet of fill to protect it from being crushed.

The size of culverts is calculated in the same way as the size of sewer pipes, computing the quantity of flow from the proper values of the acreage of the watershed and its average coefficient of runoff. The flow would be calculated for a twenty-five-year storm, or even for a greater one, since the culvert cost is small, and the consequences of an underestimate serious. As in the approximation given above for making a spot check in a sewer system, the rate would be based on an inlet time equal to the time water might take

---

* If manholes were equally spaced on the line, if they drained equal areas, and if the water flowed at a constant rate in the sewer, then this approximation would produce a slight overestimate of flow (about two percent). If downstream manholes in reality drain more area than upstream manholes, it gives greater overestimate, and vice versa. If the velocity of flow in reality speeds up in the lower reaches of the sewer, the overestimate also increases, and vice versa.

to flow halfway to the culvert from the farthest point of the drainage area, at an average speed of perhaps two feet per second, or faster in steep or barren terrain. The required culvert size then depends on the slope of the culvert itself, and on the calculated quantity of flow, as in the computations above.

Sanitary Drainage

Sanitary (a euphemism for insanitary) wastes, such as those from sinks and toilets, are generally kept out of the storm drains, but are carried down in a system quite similar in form. This waste is usually carried to a large, municipal disposal plant, which converts the sewage into an effluent that can safely be discharged into some body of natural water. The once-prevalent method of letting raw sewage flow into lakes or rivers should now be abandoned. If we cannot modify our habits of polluting water, air, and land with sewage, chemicals, fumes, and radioactive material, we may soon be able to dispense with site planning and other problems of civilization.

Sanitary drainage is typically a converging system of manholes and straight pipes, or pipes of gentle horizontal curvature, leading to a disposal plant. Unlike the storm system, it is likely to be continuous over large areas, and sometimes must be pumped up over divides in order to reach a common point of discharge. Pumping is avoided if possible at the site-planning scale. The layout of the sanitary drains may be critical at the large scale, and may affect the use of a site, but the layout itself is rarely controlling at the site-planning scale.

Unlike storm sewers, sanitary sewers form a closed drainage system connected not to open inlets, but directly to sink and toilet drains via traps which seal off the sewer odors. The branch lines leading to houses connect into the main all along its course, rather than just at the manholes. Manholes may be replaced by simple and relatively inexpensive clean-outs at the upper ends of lines, and also at branchings or breaks in alignment either of house lines or of short laterals bearing the flow of not more than 10 to 12 houses to a main sewer. Where a clean-out is used at a change in direction, the change must be less than 90°. Where two branches join at a clean-out, only one branch should change direction. Lines, particularly short laterals, need not always be entirely within the right-of-way, as long as manholes and clean-outs are accessible: a properly designed system rarely needs repair or even cleaning. Otherwise the layout technique is similar to the storm drainage system.

The minimum size of sanitary sewer pipe is set rather large in relation to rates of flow in order to prevent stoppage: eight-inch pipe for mains or laterals, and six-inch pipe for house branches. Only the main outfalls of extensive areas require a larger size of pipe. Because of the small quantities flowing in the upper ends of the system, where the pipes are much larger than capacity requires, there is a danger that slopes may not be sufficient to maintain the minimum self-cleaning velocity. Thus a standard of minimum slopes for pipes serving small numbers of houses must be set, a standard more restrictive than the storm drain minimum of 0.3 percent:

Number of houses served

	1	2	3	4	5	10	20
Minimum slope, percent	1.4	1.1	0.85	0.75	0.7	0.5	0.4

The street mains must be set low enough to receive the house laterals, dropping at these minimum gradients from the cellars of buildings. The mains are therefore likely to be set at least six feet down, and more where land slopes down from the street or where there are deep basements.

If a public disposal plant is not within reach, it is now possible to construct an economical private disposal plant, although this will generate an operation and maintenance problem. A small private plant would consist of a septic or Imhoff tank, followed by one or more sand and trickling filters. This plant should be set several hundred feet from any house, and could be economically designed to serve from 75 to 500 dwelling units.

Where soil is sufficiently pervious and ground water low, it is possible to dispense with a common drainage system in low-density development, and to give each unit a septic tank discharging into an underground drain field. Drain fields must be kept 100 feet from any surface water or well, and they should neither be heavily shaded, nor crossed by any vehicles. Their required size will depend on the absorption capacity of the soil.

Absorption capacity may be checked by digging a test pit at the drain field site in the wet season to the depth that the field will lie. Fill the pit with two feet of water, let fall to a six-inch depth, and time the drop from six to five inches. Repeat this procedure until it takes the same time to make this one-inch drop two tests running. The allowable absorption rate of the soil, in gallons per square foot of drain field area per day, is:

Time for 1 inch fall, minutes	Absorption rate, gals. per sq. ft. per day
5 or less	2.5
8	2.0
10	1.7
12	1.5
15	1.3
22	1.0

If the time of fall is much longer, it is doubtful if a drain field is usable. Given the rate, the necessary total field area can be calculated in a housing development by assuming that total sewage flow will equal 100 gallons per person per day.

If properly installed, septic tanks should give no future trouble, and are more economical than a sewage system complete with disposal plant. The small community disposal plant has the advantages that it can later be hooked into a future public system, with no loss on the investment in the sewers themselves. Either system, however, tends to make future extension of public sewers more difficult to justify economically.

Water Supply

The potability, quantity, and pressure of water supplied to residents of an area are vital to their health and convenience. Yet, while the water supply may make the development of a given site either feasible, costly, or impossible, it rarely imposes controls on the pattern of the site plan itself. The pipes of a pressure system can be laid with bends and gentle curves, and can easily be adapted to most layouts.

Water lines leak or break rather frequently and therefore must always be located in the public right-of-way, and preferably close to a traffic pavement that can carry repair vehicles. Secondly, care must be taken to prevent contamination. The mains for potable water are directly connected to using fixtures via house laterals, and cross connections with other lines must be guarded against. Sewer lines are laid below water mains, and where possible on the opposite side of the street, or ten feet distant horizontally.

As with any pressure system, there are two basic distribution layouts which may be used. One is a tree-like pattern, with lines branching out from the point of entry. A second is a loop or interconnected network, which may have more than one point of entering supply. The tree-like pattern is likely to minimize length of line, and thus be cheapest, but the loop or network is much the preferable system, since it avoids the drop in pressure at the ends of long branches and the difficulty of keeping dead-end pipes clear, while few or no units will be cut off from service when a main breaks. Where dead ends do occur, as at the ends of culs-de-sac, hydrants or blow-offs must be installed to allow occasional cleaning.

Since this utility is the one most seriously affected by frost, it is normally laid in New England under five feet of cover. The line may rise and fall with the slope of the surface, as long as positive pressures are maintained at the high points. Since water supply is paid for by quantity delivered, meters are installed in the line at individual dwellings, at groups of dwellings, or at the boundary of an entire development. Valves are placed in house branches where they leave the mains, and in mains at points necessary to cut off sections in event of breaks. Valves must be no more than 1000 feet apart. Fire hydrants are put along vehicular ways at intersections and other points, so that all parts of buildings may be reached by hose lines not over 500 feet long from one and preferably two hydrants. Yet to keep them usable in case of fire, no hydrant should be closer than 25, preferably 50, feet from any structure. In high-value commercial districts, a special high-pressure system for fire-fighting is sometimes installed separately from the potable supply.

Size of Water Pipe

The minimum diameter for water mains is eight inches, and six inches for branches. Computation of required pipe size is complex. In developments of up to moderate size, however, the eight-inch main is usually adequate. Pipe size is based on the requirement of delivering maximum instantaneous demand while maintaining minimum pressure. The latter is usually given as being 20 pounds per square inch at the hydrant or dwelling. Maximum instantaneous demand is the sum of the demand for fighting a fire and the maximum demand for domestic use, unless there is a separate fire-fighting supply. On the basis of the probability of simultaneous demand, maximum domestic use declines from 40 gallons per minute for one house, to nine gallons per minute per dwelling unit for ten houses, to two-and-a-half gallons per minute per unit for 100 houses, and to one gallon per minute per unit for 1000 houses. Fire demand may be estimated from the formula:

$$Q(\text{g.p.m.}) = 1020 \sqrt{P \left[1 - \sqrt{\frac{P}{100}} \right]}$$

where P is the population in thousands of people.

Pipe size for any one piece of line is estimated by finding the diameter which will deliver the quantity wanted with no more than the allowable pressure loss in the line. The allowable pressure loss is the entering pressure minus the desired leaving pressure, minus pressure losses in meters and valves, and plus or minus the pressure gain or loss due to rise or fall of the pipe. Since each portion of pipe is interconnected with an entire grid, whose flows and characteristics also affect the terminal conditions, the problem is usually indeterminate in form. In site planning work, where the sizing and detailing of the system is left to specialists, layout of the water system is usually confined to location of the lines, valves, meters, and hydrants in the public right-of-way. This rarely calls for changes in the design itself.

In rural or low-density developments, individual wells can take the place of a common water supply. Unlike septic tanks, they are not recommended except where unavoidable. They are generally unreliable, often expensive, and not easily supervised to maintain purity. A private group water supply is quite feasible, and its maintenance can be supported by water charges on the users. Such a system, consisting of a well, or group of wells, a pump, and a pressure or gravity tanks, can serve developments of 50 to 500 houses. The wells must be at least 100 feet from the nearest sewer or drain field. There is a break point in cost at about 200 dwelling units, where more than one well must usually be put in. But the principal cost is in the distribution system, rather than the pump or well. A large and professionally operated public water system is still the preferable solution wherever possible.

Electric Power

Power is brought in on primary high-voltage lines, and then is stepped down at transformers to enter secondary low-voltage lines going to points of use. Since low-voltage transmission is wasteful, secondary runs should be kept down to 400 feet, with transformers placed in the center of the load. As with the water system, the electric lines may follow either a branching pattern, fanning out from the point of entry to the points of use, or a loop distribution. The first is cheapest, the second preferable, although the difference is not so important as it is in the water system.

The conductors may be placed overhead on poles or underground in raceways. Underground distribution may be two to five times more expensive in first cost, but it reduces breaks, does not interfere with trees, and eliminates the clutter of poles. Once breaks occur, however, they take longer to repair when underground and cause more disruption. Power poles when located on the street are also useful for mounting street lights, telephone lines, signs, and call boxes. Nevertheless, consumers may often be willing to pay the premium for underground electric lines for visual reasons. Costs of underground installation are most favorable in light soil, and new techniques of laying cable are making them more favorable. Where there is rock or a high water table the cost difference is likely to be prohibitive, and poles therefore become mandatory.

If the overhead system is used, it is even cheaper to string the secondary lines on the buildings when siting permits it. But this entails a risk to building repairmen and adventurous children. Normally, all lines but those directly entering the structure are strung on poles, which are guyed at changes in direction and at the ends of lines, and which are spaced 125 feet apart or less. Transformers are hung on poles, or installed partially or wholly underground, with exterior venting. Where poles or raceways do not follow streets, an eight-foot easement is required. The choice of putting pole lines on the street or at rear lot lines is usually dictated by whatever minimizes the length of secondary runs. Placing poles at the rear to "beautify" the street is questionable where dwellings are low, since the poles are even more prominent on the skyline than when directly overhead. Poles at the rear lot lines are also more difficult to service.

Exterior lighting is required on public ways in all but low-density development. This is needed for safety and control, particularly at such points as intersections, steps, dead ends, or remote walkways. Powerful lights high in the air give an even illumination, but produce a general pallor that may light up houses unpleasantly. A common rule for residential streets is that lights should be spaced about 10 to 12 times their mounting height, which must be correlated with nearby buildings and planting. If electric wires are strung on poles along the street, these same poles are used for street lights. Otherwise, special poles must be erected.

Wherever placed, power and light poles are an obvious part of the visual scene. The designer should insist where he can that these poles be as handsome as the other main features of his landscape, and this requires that they be sited and designed for visual effect. The location and intensity of street lighting will have a predominant effect on the night landscape, as noted in Chapter 5, and it should be studied from that viewpoint. Street lighting has generally been guided by one simple rule: as even and as high a level of illumination as possible over every square inch. The result has been ghastly.

Page 62

Other Utilities

Gas is piped underground in a system similar to the water distribution network, in a branching or a loop pattern, with its own valves and meters. The pipes are of small diameter. The principal problem is the danger of leakage or explosion, and thus lines must not be laid under or close to buildings except when entering them, nor in the same trench with electric cable.

Telephone lines are strung overhead on the electric power poles, if the voltage characteristics of the power lines are suitable. Otherwise telephone lines are rather easily laid in underground conduits, or more simply as buried cable.

Where central heating is provided, the heating medium, usually high temperature steam, is distributed in insulated underground pressure mains, equipped with valves and set in raceways, or running through the basements of structures. Space is required for a central plant in one of the structures, or in a structure of its own. This will have a tall stack and provision for large fuel deliveries. Its location is preferably in the middle of the land, on low ground to facilitate the return of condensate.

The choice between central or group heating plants, management operated, and individual plants, tenant or owner operated, as well as the choice of fuel to be used, is an economic problem. It depends on the type and number of dwelling units, the attitude of residents, maintenance costs, the relative efficiency of plants, and the relative cost of coal, gas, oil, or electricity. A central plant is worth investigating when dealing with from 100 to 200 families or more. The choice has an important effect on the site plan. When individual plants are used, provision must be made for the delivery and storage of fuel. If coal is burned, it should be possible to chute it directly from truck to bin over no more than 20 feet. Hoses on oil delivery trucks have a maximum reach of from 100 to 200 feet. Gas and electricity can be brought directly into the unit.

In general, the location of all utilities must be considered together, avoiding cross connections, minimizing trenching, and keeping required separations between incompatible systems. In particular, the layout must be checked in three dimensions, to see that crossings in plan will not result in actual intersections below ground.

Where curves or grades allow it, it is desirable to keep utilities in a uniform location relative to the street, and also to put them underneath the planting strip, to prevent periodic digging in the road. In intensive development, where utility systems are numerous and of large capacity, it may save installation and maintenance cost if groups of them are placed in a common conduit, big enough to allow men to enter and inspect the lines. Where the site plan consists of fairly continuous structures under single control, it is sometimes better to run utility lines, except for gas, in basements or crawl spaces. This saves excavation and simplifies repairs.

Large quantities of solid waste must be removed from any inhabited area, including organic material and combustible and noncombustible rubbish. These may be picked up in varying combinations and at various times. Some of this material may be destroyed on the site in incinerators. Group collection stations may be used if they are screened and drained, but separate collection from each dwelling unit is preferable except in high density apartment structures, where incinerators may be used. For separate collection, a drained and protected area must be provided for the waste cans, convenient to the dwelling unit and as close to the curb as possible. The route from the waste cans to curb should not be too steep, and preferably should be paved. If structures are close to the road, it is possible to put waste containers within the unit, so that they can be filled from inside, and can be picked up and emptied from outside.

A note on rainfall formulas:

Where rate of rainfall formulas are not available, an approximation may be constructed from local rainfall data, if the total fall at the end of two different intervals after the beginning of a storm is known for the worst storm to be expected in two, five, ten, twenty, or whatever, years. This may even be done roughly if the fall at the end of only one interval is known, as will be seen below.

The general formula is assumed to have the form

$$I = \frac{k}{t + c}$$

which fits many storms fairly well. The arbitrary constant c sets the slope of the curve of slackening intensity while k sets the absolute quantities. The smaller c is, the more intensive the initial burst of rain, and the more quickly it slacks off. Thus, for any given total quantity, a smaller c requires a larger sewer to carry the more intensive initial pulse of run-off, unless there is storage upstream. The general formula may be fitted to any two known points on the curve as follows:

Assume that you know how much rain had fallen after five minutes (T_5), and after sixty minutes (T_{60}) of the worst storm to be expected in ten years. Begin by guessing at a value for c, and then find the two quantities W_{60} and W_5, which are:

$$W_{60} = \log_e \frac{c + 60}{c}$$

$$W_5 = \log_e \frac{c + 5}{c}$$

If c is correctly chosen, then $\dfrac{W_{60}}{W_5}$ is closer to the value $\dfrac{T_{60}}{T_5}$ than will be given by any other integral value of c. Two or three trials will give the closest value: rainfall formulas in the United States use values of c between about 10 and 35.

Sometimes only one point on the rainfall curve is known, but not two. Then c cannot be calculated, since the slope of the curve is unknown. In this case, simply assume a value: $c = 20$ is a reasonable guess.

Once c has been calculated or assumed, then k in the general formula may be derived from any one of the known rainfall points:

$$k = \frac{60\,T_{60}}{W_{60}} \quad \text{or,} \quad k = \frac{60\,T_5}{W_5}$$

The general formula for the ten-year storm,

$$I = \frac{k}{t + c}$$

is now complete.

The method is usable whatever two points on the curve are known. If these points were the fall after twenty minutes and two hours, then:

$$W_{120} = \log_e \frac{c + 120}{c}$$

$$W_{20} = \log_e \frac{c + 20}{c}$$

$$\frac{W_{120}}{W_{20}} \cong \frac{T_{120}}{T_{20}}$$

and

$$k = \frac{60\,T_{120}}{W_{120}} \cong \frac{60\,T_{20}}{W_{20}}$$

These differ from the first equations only by using the proper number of minutes in the equations for W. Note that the value 60 in the equation for k is *not* changed, since it refers to a conversion of inches per hour to inches per minute.

Chapter 13

Soil, Plants, and Climate

Subsoil

The subsurface characteristics of a site may be checked directly by superficial pits or deeper borings, or gleaned from the examination of previous structures and excavations, or from the study of old records, aerial photographs, soil maps, and geological reports. The subsurface material and its structure, and the presence of water, are the key data in analyzing earthwork and foundations. If rock is encountered, the critical technical distinction is whether it is hard and must be removed by blasting, or sufficiently soft and loose to be excavable directly by power equipment. Some shales, weak conglomerates, and highly weathered rocks are of the latter type.

The elementary constituents of soils can be very simply classified by grain size, and as to whether they are organic or inorganic. The following breakdown is the one that most directly correlates with their engineering characteristics:

1. *Gravel:* grains over 2 mm. in diameter. A well drained, stable material.
2. *Sand:* 0.05 to 2 mm. grain diameter. It is gritty to touch, especially to the teeth, and has no cohesion when dry. Pure sand is a well-drained, good foundation material, but

one that must be confined at the sides. Fine sands saturated with water can become "quick" and flow like a liquid.

3. *Silt:* 0.005 to 0.05 mm. grain diameter. This feels smooth to the touch; it has little cohesion when dry; the grains are barely visible. If silt is shaken when wet, water comes to the surface but is absorbed when the soil is squeezed. Pure silt is treacherous and unstable when wet; it may dilate; it heaves badly when frozen. But it is stable when dry or damp.

4. *Clay:* under 0.005 mm. grain diameter. The colloidal grains are invisible; it is plastic when damp and manipulated, cohesive when dry and stiff, and its frost action is mild. It is impervious, and may slip, swell, or soften when wet.

5. *Peat and Muck:* soils of organic origin regardless of grain size. They typically have a fibrous texture and are dark brown or black in color. They have a marked odor when heated. Organic soils have little friction or cohesion, are marked by capillarity and elasticity, and cannot support loads. Usually they must be removed.

Identification of Soil Types

Natural soils, of course, are almost always a mixture of these constituents, and have many complicating features of density, consistency, moisture content, structure, and drainage. For rough field identification, and a quick estimate of engineering implications, natural soils may be divided into six major classes:

> clean sands and gravels
> silty and clayey sands and gravels
> inorganic clays, sandy, silty or gravelly clays
> inorganic silts and fine sands
> organic silts and clays
> peat and muck

Samples of the subsoil may be taken in preliminary explorations from small pits, or by means of open-ended pipes driven into the ground. The thin mantle of organic topsoil may be disregarded. It is also useful to drive a $5/16$-inch by five-foot pointed rod into the ground to gauge soil density or the depth of peat, or to test for the presence of ledge or boulders. Later, it will probably be necessary to take regular borings, if major structures are contemplated, or if the ground is suspicious. Borings are generally taken at fifty-foot intervals, and to depths at least twenty feet below eventual foundations.

Preliminary soil samples may be identified in the field as follows: if less than half the soil passes a number 200 sieve, it is a sand or gravel. This sieve passes those grains which are just barely visible. The distinction may be made visually, when the soil is spread out on a flat surface. If the division is close, a sample may be put with water in a test tube and thoroughly shaken. The largest grains will settle out first, and in 20 to 30 seconds the finest sand, the material which would have just not passed the number 200 sieve, will have settled out. The volume of this coarse material may be compared to the original volume of the whole.

If the soil is a sand or gravel, it is called "clean" if there is very little fine material; and "silty or clayey" if an appreciable amount of such fine material (over about ten percent) is visible.

If the soil is not a sand or gravel, it must be tested further. Spread out a sample, and pick out all the coarse material larger than about $\frac{1}{64}$-inch diameter. Wet the remaining soil until it is putty-like, but not sticky. Make up pats of soil about half a cubic inch in size. Test for the following three characteristics:

1. *Dilatancy:* shake a pat horizontally and sharply, then squeeze it. Rapid dilatancy is exhibited when water quickly appears on the surface when shaken, and as quickly disappears when squeezed.

2. *Toughness:* roll a pat into a $\frac{1}{8}$-inch thread, fold, and re-roll it until it crumbles. Then knead it into a lump until it crumbles again. The tougher the thread and stiffer the lump just before crumbling, the higher the toughness. Medium toughness occurs when it is easy to roll a tough thread, but the lump crumbles rather readily. Soils of low toughness make weak threads, and cannot be lumped into a coherent mass.

3. *Dry strength:* allow a pat to dry in the sun and air. Crumble the dry pat between the fingers. Soils of low strength crumble readily; those of medium strength require considerable finger pressure to be brought to a powder; those of high strength can be broken but not powdered in the fingers.

Three more soil classes may now be identified from the table following:

	Dilatancy	*Toughness*	*Dry Strength*
inorganic clays, etc.	none	medium to high	medium to high
inorganic silts, etc.	slow to rapid	none to medium	none to medium
organic silts and clays	none to slow	low to medium	low to high

A preponderance of sand, silt, or clay in the fine material can also be judged by biting a sample. Sand feels gritty, silt is smooth, and clay sticks to the teeth. A predominantly organic soil may be identified by its texture, color, odor, and location. It is likely to be found in low, swampy places.

Implications of Soil Types

This classification of soils has the following implications for site planning:

The inorganic silts and the organic silts and clays are liable to frost heave, the inorganic clays less so. Where the former two types are present, foundations must always go below the frost line, and road pavements must be built to withstand or to accommodate themselves to this motion. Loose silts, into which the $\frac{5}{16}$-inch rod may easily be driven by hand, may compress and settle under loads, and if saturated may liquefy and flow. Erosion of silt is likely to be severe. Loess, or wind laid silt, which is cohesive although of low density, may if wetted collapse internally, but it is strong when dry and maintains a vertical face. Yet if kept free of water, all these soils are quite acceptable.

Medium to hard clays, which cannot be imprinted with the finger, or only with strong pressure, are strong bearing soils. Soft clays, which can be pinched in two between thumb and finger, may compress under loads, as may organic silts and clays. Clays which are both hard and dry may swell dangerously when wet. Dull gray clays or those of mottled color have very poor internal drainage and are particularly impervious.

Sands and gravels are generally best for engineering work, because of their stability and good drainage. But fine sands or sand-silt mixtures may become "quick" and flow when wet. If sands and gravels are loose, they may initially settle under loads. Where they contain appreciable fines, they lose much of their good internal drainage.

These characteristics may be summarized in another way, since the most important implications of soils in residential development are threefold: their effects on building foundations, on road construction, and on drainage, particularly in storm drainage and in sewage disposal fields.

For foundations in undisturbed soil, the sands and gravels are best, followed by the medium to hard clays, then the silts, the soft clays, and the organic silts and clays. Peat is not suitable. The clays must be watched for swelling, the silts for frost heaves, the soft clays and organic silts and clays for compression under load. In general, it is better to avoid foundations in filled ground, but, if well compacted, the sands and gravels are acceptable, the other soils less so. In this case, the organic silts and clays, as well as peat, are unacceptable. All these comments refer to foundations for buildings of three stories or less.

As base or sub-base material for residential roads, the clean sands and gravels are best, while those with fines are usually quite acceptable, at least in the sub-base. The clays, silts, and the organic silts and clays are usable in the sub-base, being desirable in that order. Peat is unusable. The poorer types must be compensated for by particularly strong or elastic pavement surfaces. The same comments about frost heave, swelling, and compression apply as in the preceding paragraph on foundations. If it is desired to stabilize the soil by the use of additives, the sands and gravels show very marked hardening, the silts marked hardening, and the clays substantial hardening. It is not economical to use additives with peat or with the organic silts and clays.

Page 203

Clean sands and gravels are the best drained, and are therefore probably usable for sewage drain fields. All other soil types must be checked by a test for absorptive capacity before they are used, but it is likely that the other sands and gravels, as well as the silts, will be usable. Some clays may be possible, but it is likely that others, as well as peat and the organic silts and clays, will not. Drain fields in fill should be avoided where at all feasible, but it is possible that clean sands and gravels, well compacted and laid over equally coarse soil, will serve. Sands and gravels with fines may also serve, but must be tested. It is most likely that all other soil types will be unacceptable for drain fields when in fill.

Not only are the natural soils a mixture of the elementary constituents, but they are irregularly deposited, and have internal structure. Soil type may change within short horizontal or vertical distances, and must be checked at many points. Where types are mixed intimately, the char-

stantially increase foundation costs. In areas of permafrost, the erection of heated buildings on the frozen ground may bring on all the problems of a saturated soil.

Earthwork Computation

The contour-area method is the simplest way of computing cut and fill, once a grading plan has been prepared. There are other more accurate methods, but this one is adequate for general quantity estimates. It has the advantage of fitting in with the development of the grading plan, and of giving a good graphic picture of the quantity and location of earthwork.

The first step is to make an earthwork diagram on the grading plan. Bring out the new contours where they differ from the old, and draw the boundary lines of no-cut, no-fill. These are drawn by interconnecting the points where new contours rejoin the old ones, and represent the edge of the disturbed land, or the boundaries between adjacent regions of cut and fill. Along these lines the new surface corresponds exactly with the old. Shade the areas between old and new contours at each level, using one color for cut, and another for fill. This is the result:

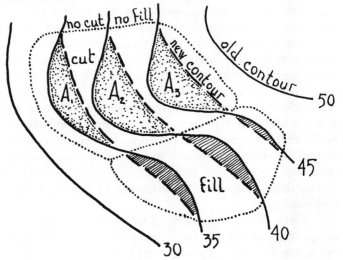

This diagram in itself gives a good visual image of the amount and balance of cut and fill, since the quantities are related to the sum of the shaded areas. It also gives a sense of the average depth of cut or fill, since where the shaded areas almost touch, the depth is almost one contour interval;

acteristics of the worst must be assumed. Soil structure refers to the layering or clustering of soil particles, and the
presence of slippage planes or holes. These may affect bearing strength and drainage. The size of boulders and the
depth to bedrock will also be meaningful.

The Presence of Water

Perhaps the most important variant of all is the presence
or absence of water: the moisture content of the soil, its
internal and surface drainage, and the position of the water table.

The water table is the underground surface below
which all interstices between soil grains are filled with water.
Normally this is a sloping, flowing surface, which roughly
follows the ground levels above, and slopes down to ponds,
lakes, streams, seeps, or springs, where it intersects the
ground surface. Its depth below ground can vary markedly,
however, and can fluctuate seasonally or over longer periods. Impervious subsurface rock or soil layers can also
modify the water table, trapping water above or below
themselves, or guiding it through seams.

See below

The water table is important for water supply and for
vegetation. Its engineering significance lies in the difficulties
caused by a high table in excavation work, as well as the
problems of flooded basements, flooded utilities, and unstable foundations. A high table is indicated by water levels
in existing wells and diggings, by seeps and springs, and by
the presence of such water-loving plants as willows, poplars,
and reeds. A six-foot test pit in the wet season will reveal the
presence of a table high enough to cause trouble in ordinary
residential development. The presence of underground water
courses is particularly critical, and structures should not be
sited over them. Avoid filling over and blocking existing
surface drainage courses: culverts must be put in to allow
continued flow.

In general, the most critical subsurface problems, the
danger flags calling for closer investigation, may be summarized as follows: a high water table; the presence of peat
and other organic soils, or of soft clay, loose silt, or fine
water-bearing sand; rock lying close to the surface; lands
previously used as dumps or containing new and unconsoli-
dated fill; or any evidence of slides or subsidence. Total site
improvement costs may increase 25 percent in rocky land,
and 85 percent in peat or muck. The latter may also sub-

where they overlap, it is more than one interval; and where they are widely spaced, depths are shallow.

If the shaded areas in any one continuous cut or fill figure (within one no-cut, no-fill boundary) are measured with a planimeter, then the volume of that cut or fill is easily approximated by multiplying the contour interval by the sum of the successive shaded areas between old and new contours at each level. In the diagram shown, if the contour interval were five feet, then the total volume of cut, V, in cubic feet, would be approximately $V = 5(A_1 + A_2 + A_3)$, where A_1, A_2, and A_3 were measured in square feet.

In order to avoid the purchase of fill or its discard, the relative balance of cut and fill is estimated. The loss of volume in transport and in the compaction of newly filled earth must be accounted for in this process. It is customary to reduce the material available from cut by five or ten percent, for comparison with the required fill. Where balance is lacking, the grading plan will have to be reworked to achieve it, unless the excess is due to some situation such as rocky ground.

Regional Climate

Any climate is complex and usually variable. Chapter 6 has set out the climatic questions that a site planner is most concerned with, particularly the distributions of air temperature, of relative humidity, and of wind direction and force, broken down by month and season. These are the fundamental data for determining effective temperature and its relation to the comfort zone. In addition, the hours of precipitation and the maximum intensities of rain indicate the need for overhead shelter and the requirements for adequate drainage. Finally, the hours of sunshine (as a percent of total possible hours), and the sun direction and elevation, indicate the measures that must be taken to invite or ward off solar radiation. Other than sun direction and elevation, the climatic factors vary irregularly from place to place. They are given overleaf in a chart for the Boston region, to illustrate what is likely to be most significant. The chart shows that outdoor temperatures are frequently above the comfort zone in July and August when the most useful cooling winds are from the southwest. Temperatures are consistently below the comfort zone from October through May, but in those two transition months the effective tem-

Page 88

Figure 40, page 220

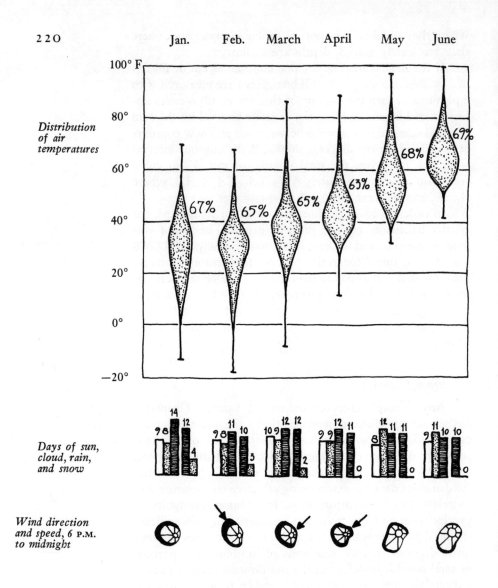

Jan. Feb. March April May June

100° F

*Distribution
of air
temperatures*

80°

67% 65% 65% 63% 68% 69%

60°

40°

20°

0°

−20°

*Days of sun,
cloud, rain,
and snow*

*Wind direction
and speed, 6 P.M.
to midnight*

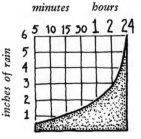

*Maximum
rate of
rainfall*

minutes   hours
5 10 15 30 1 2 24

6
5
4
3
2
1

inches of rain

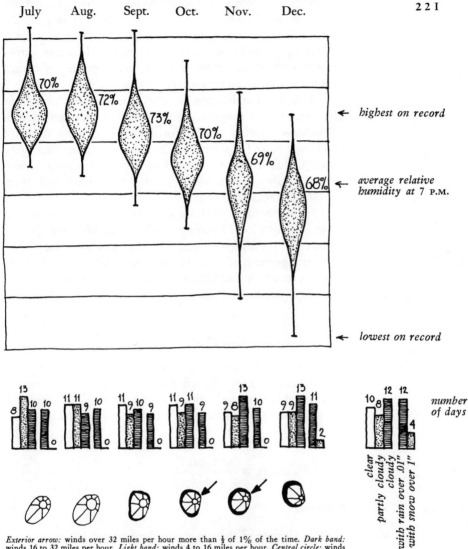

| July | Aug. | Sept. | Oct. | Nov. | Dec. |

70%
72%
73%
70%
69%
68%

← highest on record

← average relative humidity at 7 P.M.

← lowest on record

number of days

Exterior arrow: winds over 32 miles per hour more than ½ of 1% of the time. *Dark band:* winds 16 to 32 miles per hour. *Light band:* winds 4 to 16 miles per hour. *Central circle:* winds under 4 miles per hour. The length along the compass bearing, or the diameter of the central circle, is proportionate to the per cent of time that the wind is of that direction and speed.

FIGURE 40 *The climate of the Boston region by months: temperature, humidity, precipitation, sun, and wind (Sources:* House Beautiful Climate Control Guide, *Hearst Corporation, and* Climates of the States, Massachusetts, *U. S. Weather Bureau).*

peratures are often high enough to be modified successfully by using moderately warm clothing, and by changing the micro-climate. In the eight cold months the prevailing winds are stronger and come especially from the west and north-west. Sunless slopes, cold air floods, and exposure to winter winds are thus all to be avoided.

This is a humid area: precipitation occurs throughout the year, but is heaviest from December through March. Cloudiness is rather evenly distributed, but sunny days are somewhat more frequent from August to October. Strangely enough, this is also the period of highest humidity, often uncomfortably so. Cloudy days, fog, rain, snow, and damp are all to be reckoned with.

Such a general analysis, coupled with a study of the ways in which local building and habits of life have already adjusted to the climate, furnish the first clues for the choice and arrangement of the site. The data can be used much more precisely in particular situations after a careful analysis of the micro-climate.

Sun Angle and Sun Dials

The seasonal variation of sun angle depends solely on the latitude of a site. Given the latitude and the season of year, the direction and altitude of the sun may be calculated for any hour (local sun time) by these two formulas:

$$\sin Al = \cos D \cos L \cos H + \sin D \sin L$$
$$\sin Az = \frac{\cos D \sin T}{\cos H}$$

where:

$Al =$ altitude of the sun above the horizon.

$Az =$ azimuth of the sun, measured east or west from south (or from north if south of the equator).

$L =$ latitude of the place.

$D =$ declination of the sun above or below the equinoctial line, for the given season; a northerly declination being positive, and a southerly, negative (reversed in the southern hemisphere).

$H =$ local hour angle of the sun, east or west of the meridian. Each hour equals 15°, and thus $H = 0$ at noon, $H = 15°$ at 11 A.M. or 1 P.M., $H = 30°$ at 10 A.M. or 2 P.M., and so on.

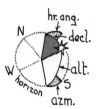

Since the movement of the sun is symmetrical, it is necessary to make these calculations for only half the day, the altitude being the same for the same hour angles in the morning or afternoon, and the azimuth also having the same values, except that it is east of south in the morning, and west of south in the afternoon.

Since the seasonal change is indicated by the change in sun declination, D, and this changes with rough regularity, it is necessary to calculate sun angles only for midwinter, midsummer, and the two equinoxes, spring and fall. These indicate the range and midpoint of sun positions, and the other times of year can be estimated between them. At the equinox $D = 0$. At the winter solstice, $D = -23°22\frac{1}{2}'$; at the summer solstice $D = 23°22\frac{1}{2}'$. (In using negative angles in the formula, keep in mind that $\sin(-\alpha) = -\sin\alpha$ but that $\cos(-\alpha) = \cos\alpha$.)

These formulas may be used for any place, any fractional time, and any particular date. For convenience, the table on page 225 gives the altitude and azimuth of the sun for various seasons for two latitudes. These may be used for rough estimates for nearby points. It is not difficult to construct a similar table for any particular place from the formulas; and this is well worth the time for important work, and for later reference for a series of designs located in the same area.

Such a table may be used to plot the shadows in plan or section for any critical time or date. They may also, and perhaps more usefully, be employed to make a simple sun dial to be used in orienting a model as described in Chapter 6. Once azimuth and altitude are known for a given latitude, such a sun dial is constructed as follows:

On a card, locate a point O, and draw line NOS, which line will represent the north-south line, while at O will be erected a vertical pin of any convenient height, P. For any given hour and season, the shadow of the top of the pin is located by drawing a line from O whose angle from north equals the azimuth of the sun from south (since the direction of the shadow opposes that of the light source) and which lies west of north in the morning, and east of it in the afternoon. Lay off a distance X along this line out from O, where:

$$X = \frac{P}{\tan Al}$$

P being the pin's height and Al the altitude of the sun. The point so obtained is the shadow tip at that hour and season.

This construction may be repeated, to give a diagram of the following form:

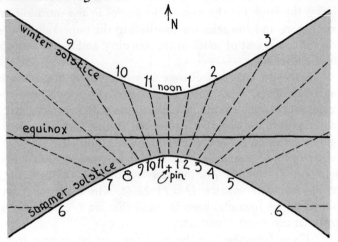

The seasonal lines (the path of the shadow tip at that season throughout the day) and the hour lines (the location of the shadow tip at that hour throughout the seasons) have been drawn by connecting the separate points for particular hours and seasons. Since the hour lines are always straight and converge on a common point on *NS* below *O*, since the equinoctial line is also straight and is at right angles to *NS*, and since the solstice lines are smooth parabolas, it is possible to sketch this diagram without actually computing all twenty-one hour and season points.

Having made the diagram, put a vertical pin at *O*, of the correct height *P*. Place the dial flat on a model, with the line *NO* parallel to the north direction on the model. If the model is now put in the sun and tilted so that the shadow of the pin's tip falls at the correct intersection of hour and season lines, or any interpolation of them, then the sunlight is falling on the model as it would do in reality at that hour, season, and latitude.

A Crude Wind Tunnel

A simple device may be made in which the general pattern of wind movement around a building group may be deduced from an architectural model. Make a rectangular box, open at both ends and large enough to contain the model. The larger the model scale, the better. Over one open end place a fine screen, and attach a funnel-shaped intake, both of which will help to smooth the flow of incoming air.

To the other end attach a large fan, which will draw air through the tunnel. Luckily, the relationship of various physical constants operating at the scale of real buildings and at that of architectural models is such that the air speed through the tunnel need not move at the correct model scale, as long as only the general wind pattern is under observation.

The tunnel may be made of glass or transparent plastic, or provided with viewing ports. If background surfaces are made matte black, and a strong cross light is directed into the tunnel, the effects are more visible. The model may now be inserted, the fan turned on, and smoke be introduced at the intake end. Smoke can be generated by a cigar, a piece of punk, a bee-keeper's smoker, or similar devices. The

ALTITUDE AND AZIMUTH OF THE SUN

Latitude 30°	Winter Solstice		Vernal & Autumnal Equinox		Summer Solstice	
Time	Azimuth	Altitude	Azimuth	Altitude	Azimuth	Altitude
6 P.M. or 6 A.M.	—	—	90°	0	111°	11°
5 P.M. or 7 A.M.	62°	0	82°	13°	104°	24°
4 P.M. or 8 A.M.	54°	11°	74°	26°	98°	37°
3 P.M. or 9 A.M.	44°	21°	63°	38°	92°	50°
2 P.M. or 10 A.M.	32°	29°	49°	49°	83°	63°
1 P.M. or 11 A.M.	17°	35°	28°	57°	67°	75°
NOON	0	36°	0	60°	0	83°

Latitude 42°

Time	Azimuth	Altitude	Azimuth	Altitude	Azimuth	Altitude
7 P.M. or 5 A.M.	—	—	—	—	117°	5°
6 P.M. or 6 A.M.	—	—	90°	0	108°	15°
5 P.M. or 7 A.M.	—	—	78°	11°	99°	26°
4 P.M. or 8 A.M.	53°	4°	69°	22°	89°	38°
3 P.M. or 9 A.M.	42°	12°	56°	32°	78°	48°
2 P.M. or 10 A.M.	29°	19°	41°	40°	63°	59°
1 P.M. or 11 A.M.	15°	23°	22°	46°	39°	68°
NOON	0	25°	0	48°	0	71°

Angles to the nearest whole degree. Altitude is the angle above the horizon; azimuth the angle east or west of south (or of north if in the southern hemisphere). Time is local sun time.

streamlines of smoke will make the general wind patterns clearly visible, and they may be photographed. The model may be turned about, to study various wind directions.

The air flows may be studied in greater detail by means of a short piece of fine white thread tied to the end of a long thin rod. As this tiny "pennant" is moved about in the model space, it will make the local air flow visible by the way it streams out, droops, flutters, flies at an angle, or even turns backwards.

No conclusions as to wind speed or force can be made by this method, but the general pattern is approximated. Strictly speaking, it is necessary to include in the model the environment some distance upwind, as well as the ground detail which acts as a brake on air flow. The effect of ground detail may be approximated by a low picket fence at the intake end, five or six feet high to the model scale. To the extent that these two precautions are neglected, the device will falsify air movements at the upwind side of the model, or immediately along the ground surface.

Plant Varieties

Exhaustive plant lists may be found in many other sources. The plants of most concern to the site planner are the ornamental trees, the primary ground covers, and the plants suitable for large hedges. These are the materials he uses to produce his spatial effects; other plants are more significant at the level of garden design.

The suitability of a plant for any position will depend on the soil and the microclimate: the drainage, acidity, and presence of humus; and the temperatures, insolation, moisture, and winds. Flourishing local flora are often a good guide to species which may be used. The plant lists to follow include species generally usable and obtainable in much of the United States. In other areas, entirely different plant materials may be needed. In many localities in the world, commercial nurseries are not developed, and plants may be suitable but simply not obtainable.

Ground Covers

The following will serve as ground covers in most of the United States:

Ajuga reptans (Carpet Bugle): deciduous perennial 4"; in sun, partial or dense shade; grows rapidly; blue flowers May.

Arctostaphylos uva-ursi (Bearberry): evergreen trailing shrub 6–8″; sun or partial shade; stony, sandy soil; dark green foliage, red berries September.

Hedera helix (English Ivy): evergreen vine, 10″; partial or dense shade; an even, solid cover of long life; will climb up anything it can reach.

Juniperus horizontalis (Prostrate Juniper): evergreen shrub, 10″; sun; slow-growing, but will form dense mat of long life.

Lysimachia nummularia (Moneywort): deciduous creeping vine under 6″; sun or shade; roots along its stems, grows rapidly; bright yellow flowers spring and summer; needs rich moist soil.

Pachysandra terminalis (Japanese Spurge): evergreen plant, 8″; partial or dense shade; permanent, grows rapidly, very reliable.

Rosa wichuraiana (Wichura Rose): trailing rose, 7½″; sun; deciduous, glossy, dark green foliage, white flowers June; spreads long distances and keeps down weeds.

Vinca minor (Periwinkle, Blue Myrtle): evergreen trailing vine, 8″; partial or dense shade; dark green leaves, blue flowers May; very dependable, grows rapidly.

To this list, of course, we must add the various varieties of grasses, mown and unmown.

Plants suitable for hedges may be trees or shrubs, evergreen or deciduous. They must have thick foliage of a fine texture, be dense close to the ground and throughout their height, and be able to withstand cutting. The following species are suitable for trimmed hedges in the United States (the two dimensions give the range of hedge height obtainable with the species):

Evergreen Hedges

Buxus sempervivens suffruticosa (Dwarf Box): 1½′–6′; dense, trims to precise lines; dark, shining green leaves, fine texture; slow growing, may be cut to ground and survive; not hardy in north.

Ilex crenata microphylla (Japanese Holly): 2½–20′; dense; slow growing, long lived, fine-textured.

Laurus nobilis (Grecian Laurel, Sweet Bay): 6′–40′; upright, tapering, dense; slow growing; large aromatic dense leaves; not hardy in north.

Pyracantha coccinea (Firethorn): 4′–12′; wide-spreading, needs space; can take severe cutting; orange-vermilion fruits in autumn.

Taxus media Hicksii (Hicks Yew): up to 8′; narrow, upright, columnar; dark green needle-like foliage; tolerant of soil, slow-growing, disease-free.

Thuya occidentalis (American Arborvitae): 8′–30′; hardy, slow-growing, needs moist air; waxy, aromatic, lichen-like leaves turning brownish in winter.

Tsuga canadensis (Canadian or Eastern Hemlock): 10′–30′; dense, takes light cutting only; long-lived; fine shiny needles, dark green above, light green below; feathery texture; shade tolerant, needs moist soil.

Deciduous Hedges

Acer campestre (Hedge Maple): up to 25′; dense.

Berberis thunbergi (Japanese Barberry): 3′–5′; thorny and dense; autumn coloring, red berries; hardy.

Carpinus betulus (European Hornbeam): 6′–20′; dense, takes pruning well.

Cotoneaster adpressa divaricata (Rockspray): 3′–6′; dense, wide-spreading; small, dark green leaves, red berries autumn.

Crataegus monogyna (Single Seed Hawthorn): up to 15′; dense, twiggy, very thorny; grows easily and takes clipping well; white flowers May, red berries.

Fagus sylvatica (European Beech): 8′–30′; dense, dark green, bronze in autumn.

FIGURE 41 *Average annual minimum temperatures for the United States* (*Source:* The Yearbook of Agriculture, *1949, U. S. Dept. of Agriculture*).

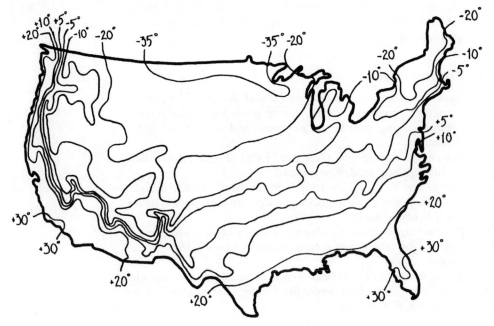

Ligustrum amurense (Amur Privet): 4'–15'; dense, fairly rapid growing; evergreen in south; trims easily.

Maclura pomifera (Osage Orange): up to 25'; may be cut to ground, vigorous; makes compact thorny mass; large orange-like green fruits; withstands drought and cold.

Tilia cordata (Littleleaf Linden): 10'–30'; dense, fine texture; bright green; yellow flowers early summer.

Trees

Finally, we list the most dependable ornamental or shade trees for urban or suburban locations, which are hardy over large areas of the United States:

Reference 48

Key:

125	height in feet commonly reached by mature specimens in favorable suburban conditions.
E	evergreen
R	grows rapidly
S	grows slowly
Hc	hardy in very dense urban areas
Ho	hardy in some other difficult situations, such as very wet or dry ground, sterile soil, shade, or the seashore.
−20°	hardy where the average annual minimum temperature is above this level (See Fig. 41, page 228).
Df	practically free of diseases and pests.
Dp	prone to diseases or infestations, requiring annual care.

Abies concolor (White Fir), 120 E, Hc Ho −20°.
Pyramidal, almost columnar, dense. Foliage to ground persists to maturity. Bluish mossy green needles in thick planes on horizontal or down sloping branches. Heavy, shadowed texture. Needs moist soil, tolerates shade. Withstands heat. Fairly rapid growth.

Acer ginnala (Amur Maple), 20, −50°.
Upright, rounded, densely branched, with dense, fine foliage, turning brilliant scarlet in autumn. Fruit turns bright red in summer. Good for screening.

Acer platanoides (Norway Maple), 90 R, Hc Ho −35°.
Broad, round headed, regular outline. Large broad leaves, medium green, smooth. Coarse texture of light and shade; deep shade under tree; difficult to grow anything under it. Clear yellow in autumn, leaves persistent. Yellow flowers April. Good street tree. Any soil, will tolerate seashore conditions. There are columnar, globose, pyramidal, and red leafed varieties.

Acer saccharum (Sugar or Hard Maple), 120 S, −35°.
Short trunk and upright branches form dense, compact, oval crown. Large deep cut leaves, smooth dark green, whitish beneath, brilliant yellow, orange, and red in autumn. Lacy yellow flowers spring. Sweet sap. Any soil. Sturdy. Finest of the maples.

Aesculus hippocastanum (Horse Chestnut), 75 R, Hc Ho −35°, Dp.
Round headed, pyramidal, visible stout stem and branch structure. Large stellate leaves, medium green. Open, coarse, feathery texture. Large creamy upright flower spikes at twig ends in late spring, like candles. Makes litter of leaves and nuts. Large varnished buds in winter, leaves open suddenly in spring. Needs moist soil. Brittle; subject to leaf scorch late summer. Tolerates seashore conditions.

Ailanthus altissima (Tree of Heaven), 60 R, Hc Ho −20°, Df.
Open form, coarsely branched, spreading. Large compound bright green leaves, malodorous when crushed. Staminate flowers also malodorous, but soon gone; pistillate flowers turn coppery red. Self-seeding, very vigorous, grows anywhere. Coarse texture, striped and dotted shade. Smoke, dust, disease resistant, roots penetrating. Tolerates salt spray, wet or dry or poor soils. Brittle.

Betula lenta (Sweet or Cherry Birch), 50, −35°, Dp.
Straight trunk, oval crown; pyramidal when young. Upper branches ascending, lower horizontal or drooping. Bright green leaves pales beneath; golden yellow in autumn. Bark reddish brown to black, cherry-like. Twigs and young bark aromatic to chew.

Carpinus caroliniana (American Hornbeam, Blue Beech, Ironwood), 35, −50°, Df.
A rounded, bushy tree with several trunks, their gray muscled bark like that of a beech. Dense foliage, turning orange to red in autumn. Difficult to transplant.

Catalpa speciosa (Northern Catalpa), 70 R, Hc Ho −20°.
Generally pyramidal, but an irregular outline. Thick, irregular, but generally horizontal branches visible. Large long-stalked light green leaves in bursts on ridged branchlets. Heavy, plastic texture, many holes. Showy spotted white flowers June and July. Long slender curving pods, persistent in winter, rattling in wind. Any soil. Withstands heat and drought.

Cercidiphyllum japonicum (Katsura Tree), 60, −20°, Df.
Broad, spreading dome; loose, willowy outline. Stout, crooked, climbable branches. Dark green leaves close to branches. Strong texture. Air circulates freely through the tree. Can be made columnar in habit. Yellow and scarlet in autumn. Moist soil.

Cercis canadensis (Eastern Redbud), 35, −20°.

Flat topped, irregular, of loose outline. Foliage of a fine, open texture, yellow in autumn. Small purplish pink flowers in clusters, in early spring.

Cladastris lutea (Yellow Wood), 40, −35°.

Full, rounded figure, ascending limbs diverge from short, smooth trunk. Bark like beech. Large compound leaves, bright yellow green; orange to yellow in autumn. Creamy flowers in long hanging clusters, fragrant, in May and June.

Cornus florida (Flowering Dogwood), 40, −20°, Df.

A flat-topped, horizontally branching tree, the dense and lustrous foliage appearing in a series of level planes, scarlet in autumn. Large white flower bracts in May, bright red berries in the fall. One of the best of the small ornamental trees.

Crataegus phaenopyrum (Washington Hawthorn), 30, Hc −20°, Dp.

Broadly columnar in habit, thorny, densely branching and twiggy, eventually round headed. Dense, lustrous leaves, turning scarlet to orange in autumn. White flowers in clusters in June; bright red berries persistent all winter. Difficult to transplant, requires yearly attention to keep free of pests.

Elaeagnus angustifolia (Russian Olive), 20, Hc Ho −50°, Df.

A wide-spreading, rather open tree, with distinctive, narrow, gray-green leaves. Unique crooked trunk with brown, shedding bark. Small, silvery, fragrant flowers in early June. Tolerant of seashore and city conditions, and many kinds of soil.

Fagus sylvatica (European Beech), 80, −20°.

A great solid, spreading, oval tree. Needs growing room. Branches sweep ground, forming hollow within. Dense, dark green, small, thin, shining leaves: bronze and persistent in autumn. Gray smooth bark like muscled skin, heavy trunk and branches. Dark full texture, a massive sculptural tree. Rather dry soil but tolerant. Long-lived. Can be trimmed for hedges. There are fastigiate, weeping, and copper- or purple-leaved varieties.

Fraxinus americana (White Ash), 80 R, Hc −35°, Dp.

Tall stem, compact long oval head with regular outline, stout ascending branches, fairly high off ground. Large pinnate leaves, a dense rich texture striped with light and shade. Grass grows well beneath it. A stately tree. Deep purple or yellow in autumn. Tolerant of soil. Seeds self vigorously. Must be sprayed for oyster scale.

Gingko biloba (Gingko), 80 R, Hc −20°, Df.

Tall, conical, but sparse outline; side branches diagonally erect. Fan shaped leaves on short twigs, leathery dark green, yellow in autumn. Fruit on pistillate tree malodorous, but pit is edible. An ancient and picturesque tree. There is a columnar variety.

Gleditsia triacanthos inermis moraine (Moraine Locust), 100 R, Hc −20°, Df.

Round headed, rigid horizontal branches, lacy compound foliage, feathery but regular outline, open underneath, light shade. No thorns or pods on this variety. Leaves appear late in spring and drop off early in fall. Long-lived.

Gymnocladus dioica (Kentucky Coffee Tree), 80 R, −20°, Df.

Graceful asymmetrical form, open underneath, coarse twigs, prominent scaly bark. Large compound leaves, medium green. A light feathery open texture. Green-white flowers in large clusters; long thick curved pods which litter ground. Rich soil.

Juniperus virginiana (Eastern Red Cedar), 60 E S, Ho −50°, Df.

Narrow, upright, compact. Can vary from 120 feet to a bush, depending on soil and climate. Tiny, scale-like or pointed, dark green leaves, aromatic, persistent for several years, gradually turning brown, giving a rusty overtone. A dark, fine, but rather open texture. Bark thin, red, stringy. Dark blue berries attract birds. Tolerates seashore and any soil but a swamp.

Liquidambar styraciflua (Sweet Gum, Red Gum), 80, Ho −20°, Df.

Rather erect and oblong, but irregular in outline. Crooked, ridged heavy branches, ascending from tall straight trunk. Large, glossy, star-shaped leaves, turning brilliant scarlet and crimson in autumn. Fragrant sap. Large, ball-shaped, persistent fruit.

Liriodendron tulipifera (Tulip Tree), 150, −20°, Df.

Tall, straight stem, short branches high from ground. Oblong but irregular outline. Broad shining leaves, pale beneath, turning clear yellow in autumn. An open, spotted, trembling texture. Tulip-like flowers in June, greenish yellow with orange markings. Rich moist soil. Long-lived.

Magnolia acuminata (Cucumber Tree), 90 R, −20°, Df.

Stately formal pyramid, wide-spreading in age. Small gray branches visible. Very large, thin, smooth, yellow green leaves, brown in autumn. Strong play of light and shade in texture, dark shade underneath. Large yellowish-green, bell-shaped, erect flowers late spring.

Malus floribunda (Japanese Flowering Crab Apple), 30, −20°, Dp.

Rounded, densely branched, branches close to ground on all sides. Dense, fine texture. Flowers deep pink to red, fading to white, fragrant, in early May. Yellow and red fruit in fall. A dependable flowering tree.

Nyssa sylvatica (Sour or Black Gum, Tupelo, Beetlebung), 80, Ho −20°.

Erect, cylindrical or pyramidal, rounded crown, but variable. Short, rigid, crooked, twiggy branches; bold winter outline. Rough, dark bark. Leaves leathery, dark green, shining, turning flaming red in autumn. Fruit attracts birds. Shallow roots, wind may uproot tree if exposed. Wet soil. Tolerates seashore.

Phellodendron amurense (Amur Cork Tree), 40 R, Hc −35°, Df.

Low rounded outline, open interior. Low trunk; spreading, picturesque, corky, climbable branches, highly visible. Compound leaves, medium green, aromatic, appearing late. Planes of light and shade, a very linear texture. Abundant, persistent, black fruit. Light shade.

Picea pungens (Colorado Blue Spruce), 80 E S, Hc Ho −50°, Dp.

Stiffly pyramidal. Dense bluish green foliage of strong hard color, especially the new growth. Needles rigid, spiny. Long lived: in age loses pyramidal shape and blue color and lower branches drop off. Tolerates shade. Moist soil. Needs spraying for pest control. Best in early years of life.

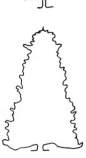

Pinus nigra (Austrian Pine), 90 E R, Ho −20°.

Pyramidal when young, later flat topped with spreading branches. Horizontal branches in whorls, from close to ground; regular outline, dense foliage on exterior, open within; yellow brown scaly bark. Long stiff thick needles, dull dark green. A heavy, dark, sombre tree. Good wind screen; tolerates seashore and acid soil.

Pinus resinosa (Red or Norway Pine), 75 E R, Ho −50°.

Tall straight pyramidal tree, branched to ground, becoming wide-spreading when older. Stiff drooping branches, reddish scaly bark. Rather open outline and interior. Long soft coarse needles, shining dark green. An open, needly, gnarled texture. Long-lived, fairly disease resistant, hardy, will tolerate rocky sandy soil. Needs full sun. Very rapid growth.

Pinus strobus (White Pine), 125 E R, −35°, Dp.

First a symmetrical pyramid; then tall and rather cylindrical; finally of picturesque wide-spreading outline in old age. Horizontal, open branches in regular whorls from tall dark gray stem. Long soft green needles in massive horizontal planes of softly shaded, sculptural texture. Ground beneath carpeted with brown needles, intersected with twisting roots. Any moist but drained soil, needs sun. Long-lived, may grow very tall, but can be pruned. Subject to white pine blister rust. A majestic tree.

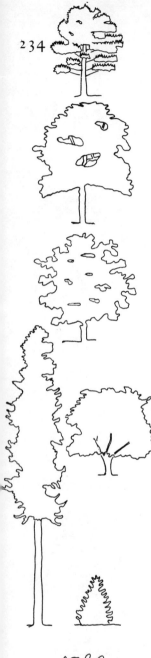

Pinus sylvestris (Scotch Pine), 75 E, Ho — 50°.

Open, pyramidal when young; round-topped, irregular and picturesque when old. Stiff bluish-green needles, red bark on older wood. Unique form and color. Seashore hardy.

Platanus acerifolia (London Plane Tree), 100 R, Hc —10°.

Round headed, upright stem, spreading branches, deep shade beneath. Mottled gray and creamy trunk. Dense foliage, large maple-like leaves, light green. Easily clipped. A shapely tree with a cheerful spotted play of light and shade. Best in rich moist soil, but tolerant. Very similar to the sycamore.

Populus alba (White Poplar), 90 R, Hc Ho —35°, Df.

A wide-spreading, irregular, rather open habit. Foliage gray-ish-green above, downy white below, making for interesting play of light in a breeze. Whitish-gray bark. Very rapid growth, but weak wooded, and the roots penetrate every-where. Tolerates the city, the seashore, wet and very dry ground. Only to be used where other trees will not grow, or as rapid growing fillers until better trees are established. A columnar variety is a good substitute for the Lombardy Pop-lar, which is subject to a trunk canker.

Prunus sargenti (Sargent Cherry), 75, —20°, Dp.

Upright, dense, with a rounded top. The dense foliage first appears bronze, matures to green, and turns red in autumn. Tree is covered with deep pink flowers in late April, before the leaves appear. Interesting dark, shining, figured bark. Dense shade. Must be sprayed once a year to control pests, needs full sun. Wood liable to split in heavy winds or ice. Cherries are normally rather short-lived, but this is a longer-lived variety, one of the best of the cherries. A fine ornamental.

Pseudotsuga taxifolia (Douglas Fir), 250 E, —20°, Df.

A regular pyramid with branches to ground when young; in age a towering stem with relatively small branches at top, and clear of them for ⅓ of height to ground. Very long-lived: 400–750 years. Soft blue-green needles on pendant branchlets; a dense fine texture. Can be pruned. Prefers a light, rather acid soil. Moderately tolerant of shade. Rapid growth when young. Only the mountain variety is hardy to —20°.

Quercus alba (White Oak), 80 S, Ho —20°.

A rounded, ragged outline; large, crooked, wide-spreading branches. Trunk and branch structure visually dominant. Broadens with age, requires growing room. Long-lived. Rough, light gray bark; deeply cut, medium green leaves, turning russet, wine red in autumn. Leaves in clusters on the branches, persistent in winter. Best in rich moist soil, but adaptable. Tolerates seashore.

Quercus borealis (Northern Red Oak), 70 R, Hc −20°.

An irregular, round headed tree. Short massive ridged trunk divides into several stout branches, fairly high off ground. Finely cut leaves, medium green, turning dark red in autumn. A coarse, branchy texture.

Quercus palustris (Pin Oak), 75 R, −20°.

Stately, erect, cylindrical. Slender horizontal branches, down sweeping near ground. Lower branches drop off with age. Dense, deep-cut, shining green leaves, red in autumn. Best in moist, not alkaline, soil.

Quercus phellos (Willow Oak), 50 R, Hc −10°.

Rounded outline with pyramidal top. Branches ascending, lower ones persistent. Bark light red brown. Leaves leathery, willow-like, glossy green above and paler beneath, pale yellow in autumn. Wet soil. A good street tree in southern cities.

Salix elegantissima (Thurlow Weeping Willow), 40 R, −20°, Dp.

Round-topped and full, with long pendulous branches, graceful and picturesque. The foliage is fine and narrow, set on fine branches, and moves in any breeze. Weak-wooded, cracks easily. Requires moist ground; the roots penetrate and clog sewers and drains. Subject to diseases and pests, and requiring much maintenance. Use only in special situations, for the graceful and symbolic habit.

Sophora japonica (Pagoda or Scholar Tree), 75, Hc Ho −20°, Df.

A compact low round head of graceful lacy outline, becoming like Fraxinus in habit with age. Decorative, dark green pinnate leaves. Trembling delicate texture. Large clusters fragrant yellowish-white flowers August. Any soil.

Tilia cordata (Little Leaf Linden), 90, Hc Ho −35°, Dp.

Tall, rounded, broad-based, dense and regular. Branches often sweeping to ground, forming a "cave" beneath. Dark shade. Smallish bright green leaves, forming a dense, fine texture. Abundant fragrant yellow flowers in early summer, attracting bees. Rich soil, neither too wet nor dry. Tolerates seashore. A solid, handsome shade tree. Needs spraying for leaf-eating insects.

Tsuga canadensis (Canadian or Eastern Hemlock), 90 E S, Ho −35°.

Pyramidal but rather open, feathery outline; scattered horizontal branches on tall stem, persistent to ground, many small drooping branchlets. Fine short needles, shiny dark green above, light green below. A fine feathery texture, open at the edge, dark at the stem. Ridged red-brown bark. Dark shade beneath. Long-lived, shade tolerant; acid, well-drained, moist soil, cool north slopes. Takes pruning and then grows dense; much used for hedges. Many variants of different habit. One of best of the evergreens.

Chapter 14

Costs

It is fruitless to present any precise data on costs, since they would be out-dated before they were published, and even then would be applicable only to one area. Reliable cost estimates of any project can only be made by detailed calculations done by someone familiar with current costs in a given place when using a given level of technology. On the other hand, two kinds of general knowledge about costs can be of value to the site planner: a sense of what things are most critical in raising or lowering cost, and some figures which help him to make preliminary estimates or to judge between rough alternatives.

Variations in site construction costs are caused by fluctuations in the costs of labor and materials, in the skill of construction management, and in the construction technology. But variations are also caused by the nature of the site and the finesse of the design. Unfavorable site conditions may increase total site development costs by over 100%. Variations in design may shave average unit costs by as much as 20%, or inflate them by as much as 30%. To illustrate these effects, assume that one were designing a housing group with no objective other than to make it as cheap as possible. What features would it contain?

First, a site would be chosen which was neither steep nor dead level and which did not contain peat, fill, or rock close to the surface. It would have a compact shape, and adequate utilities would lie at its borders.

The general design would group the buildings compactly, using the highest density allowable for the given building type. Structure and streets would be regularly arranged so that there are no fragmentary open or waste areas. Common facilities and public open space would be deleted or kept to the allowable minimum. All open spaces, particularly publicly-maintained ones, would be as concentrated and as regularly shaped as possible. There would be no landscaping other than grass, no hard surfacing except on the roads, and no fences or retaining walls.

The streets would use a regular pattern with a minimum number of intersections, i.e., blocks would be rectangular and very large. Buildings and streets would be arranged to minimize the street length per dwelling unit, by occupying all frontages solidly, and by using such devices as double and triple building lines, or rows end-on to the street. The roads would follow topography closely, having long-radius curves and gentle (but not flat) gradients. The design would allow the separation of roads by function into major, feeder, and minor streets, and the pavements would then be made as narrow and light as possible. Parking space would be reduced and would be provided in double-loaded, perpendicular, off-street bays. There would be no street curbs, and a minimum of sidewalks.

Utility lines would have a minimum length per dwelling unit, and the provision of a storm sewer system and street lighting would be avoided. A sanitary sewer system would also be deleted if densities allowed the installation of septic tanks. Electricity and telephone lines would be carried on poles overhead or strung from building to building. Underground utilities would lie at minimum depth. No roof drains would be attached to the sewers; all utilities would be sized exactly to present loads. Electricity and water would be distributed in a branching, rather than a loop, pattern. There would be a minimum number of manholes, cleanouts, valves, hydrants, poles, transformers, and other such fixtures. Cleanouts would be used in place of manholes wherever possible.

Dwelling units themselves would have a minimum floor area. They would occur in narrow, deep, two-story row houses, or in compact three- and four-story walk-ups. There would be a minimum number of building types, arranged in a regular pattern. Buildings would be sited close to existing ground level and would not be placed on fill. They would have no breaks, offsets, or projections in plan or section.

They would have low ceiling heights, and be surfaced in inexpensive materials. They would be close to each other and to the street, using long, attached structures with minimum setbacks and end spacings.

(In this regard, it is useful to know something of the variations in site cost in current single-family development. Each extra foot that a building is set back from the street costs almost twice as much as each foot added to the depth of rear yard or block interior, and each extra foot of street frontage costs almost five times as much as that same extra foot of rear yard.)

Obviously, this is not the best way to design a residential project, but the description serves to expose the factors which affect cost. Some of the features, incidentally, may reduce immediate cost, while increasing long-run costs due to maintenance or replacement, or while creating more intangible community costs. In addition, they reflect costs only under present technology in this country, subject to present custom as to what is the tolerable minimum.

Cost Comparisons

To provide a basis for making rough cost comparisons between alternative plans, the following generalized item costs are given. They do not include the contractor's profit, his contingency margin, or professional fees. These would add 15% to 20% to the total cost. The figures are rounded off and based on costs in the Boston area in 1961. They will never be accurate for any particular job. They can only be employed for comparison, because the relative cost of items is more stable than the absolute cost. Such comparative figures will be usable for a few years until significant changes in building organization or technology upset the balance between items:

1. *Grading*

General cleaning and grubbing, per acre	$400.00
Earth cut and fill, per cubic yard moved	0.70
Additional borrow fill in place, per cubic yard	2.00
Crushed stone or gravel, in place, per cubic yard	3.00
Topsoil strip and replace, per cubic yard	1.00
Topsoil purchased and spread, per cubic yard	3.50
Rock excavation with explosives, per cubic yard	8.00
Low granite or fieldstone retaining walls, per linear foot	5.00

Concrete retaining walls five feet high
with footings (cost increases in proportion to height), per linear foot $25.00

2. *Streets, walks, bridges*

Bituminous macadam pavement, gravel
base, local street, per square foot   0.30
Concrete sidewalk, with foundation course,
per square foot   0.50
Asphalt walk, wood edging, five feet wide,
per square foot   0.20
Gravel walk, per square foot   0.05
Concrete curb and gutter, per linear foot   2.50
Granite curb, per linear foot   3.50
Small culvert, per linear foot   10.00
Bridge, less than 20 ft. span, per square foot 16.00
Bridge, 20 to 100 ft. span, per square foot 35.00

3. *Utilities*

Sewer pipe in place, per linear foot:

Depth of pipe	*Diameter of pipe*					
	6″	*8″*	*10″*	*12″*	*15″*	*18″*
Less than 6 ft.	$3.25	3.50	3.75	4.00	4.50	5.25
6–10 ft.	$3.75	4.00	4.25	4.50	5.25	6.00

Manholes (add $30.00 per foot
if over 8 ft. deep), each $225.00
Inlets, each   150.00
Cleanouts, each   75.00
6″ water pipe in place, per linear foot   4.00
6″ gate valves and boxes, each   75.00
Hydrants, each   130.00
Overhead electric power, including poles and
transformers, per linear foot of line   1.25
Underground electric power, including
transformers, per linear foot of line, park cable 4.00
in conduit   8.00

4. *Landscaping*

Seeding and fine grading, good lawn, per square
foot $0.05
Seeding and fine grading, large fields, per square
foot   0.02
Young trees, in place, each   35.00
10–12 ft. trees, in place, each   65.00
For large trees in place, figure $40.00 per inch of
diameter up to 6 inches, and $10.00 per inch
thereafter
5 foot chain link fence, per linear foot   3.50

For extremely rough first guesses, not to be used for comparisons, costs may be summarized as *acreage costs* (land price, cleaning and grubbing, general earthwork, landscaping) plus *linear costs* of the road system (fine grading, pavement and base, walks, curbs, sewer, water, electricity, lights, trees and culverts), plus *percentage costs* (profit, contingency, overhead, fees). From experience, general figures of this kind may be kept in mind for work of a certain kind at a given time and place, and rapidly applied to preliminary designs or proposals. For example, based on the costs given above, applied to normal single-family housing development in the Boston area, such rough general costs would be about $2500, plus cost of the land, for each acre developed, plus $30 for each foot of street, plus 15%. It is normal today in residential work that the total cost of site development (exclusive of structure but inclusive of raw land cost) will come to between 15% and 20% of total project cost.

Selected References on Site Planning

General References

1. American Public Health Association, Committee on the Hygiene of Housing, *Planning the Neighborhood; Standards for Healthful Housing.* Chicago, Public Administration Service, 1948.
2. Blumenfeld, Hans, "Scale in Civic Design." *Town Planning Review*, Vol. XXIV, No. 1 (1953), p. 35.
3. Gibberd, Frederick, *Town Design*, 3rd Edition. London, Architectural Press, 1959, Parts 2, 3, and 4.
4. Goldfinger, Ernö, "Sensation of Space," "Urbanism and the Spatial Order," and "Elements of Enclosed Space." *Architectural Review*, Vol. XC, Nos. 539 and 540 (November and December, 1941), and Vol. XCI, No. 541 (January, 1942).
5. Hamlin, Talbot F., *Forms and Functions of 20th Century Architecture*, Vol. I. New York, Columbia University Press, 1952, Chap. 17.
6. Hubbard, Henry V., and Kimball, Theodora, *An Introduction to the Study of Landscape Design.* New York, Macmillan, 1917.
7. Ministry of Housing and Local Government, Great Britain, *Design in Town and Village.* London, H.M.S.O., 1953.
8. Pedersen, Sverre, "Plotting and Planning of Building Sites." *International Federation of Housing and Town Planning Bulletin*, 1936.
9. Repton, Humphry, *Landscape Gardening and Landscape Architecture*, J. C. Loudon, ed. London, Longmans, 1840.
10. Simonds, John O., *Landscape Architecture, the Shaping of Man's Natural Environment.* New York, F. W. Dodge, 1961.
11. Sitte, Camillo, *The Art of Building Cities*, trans. by Stewart. New York, Reinhold, 1945 (orig. ed. 1889), Chaps. I–VII.
12. Sitwell, Sir George, *On the Making of Gardens.* New York, Scribner, 1951 (orig. ed. 1909).

Social Aspects

13. Bauer, Catherine, "Social Questions in Housing and Community Planning." *Journal of Social Issues*, Vol. 7, Nos. 1–2 (1951).
14. Dyckman, John, "On Men and Mice and Moles." *American Institute of Planners Journal*, Vol. XXVII, No. 1 (February, 1961), p. 102.
15. Festinger, "Architecture and Group Membership." *Journal of Social Issues*, Vol. 7, Nos. 1–2 (1951).

16. Gans, Herbert, J., "Planning and Social Life" and "Homogeneity or Heterogeneity in Residential Areas?" *American Institute of Planners Journal*, Vol. XXVII, Nos. 2 and 3 (May and August, 1961).
17. Jacobs, Jane, *The Death and Life of Great American Cities*. New York, Random House, 1961.
18. Kuper, Leo, "Blueprint for Living Together," in Kuper, ed., *Living in Towns*. London, Cresset Press, 1953, Chap. X.
19. Merton, Robert K., "The Social Psychology of Housing," in Dennis, ed., *Current Trends in Social Psychology*. Pittsburgh, University of Pittsburgh Press, 1948.
20. Riemer, Svend, "Hidden Dimensions of Neighborhood Planning." *Land Economics*, Vol. 26, No. 2 (May, 1950), p. 197.
21. Wallace, A. F. C., *Housing and Social Structure*. Philadelphia, Philadelphia Housing Authority, 1952.

Residential Site Planning

22. Central Mortgage and Housing Corporation, *Housing Design*. Ottawa, 1952–1953, Parts 1 and 2.
23. Kennedy, Robert Woods, *The House and the Art of Its Design*. New York, Reinhold, 1953, Chaps. IX and X.
24. Lovejoy, D. A. W., "Residential Site Planning." *Town Planning Institute Journal*, Vol. XXXIV, No. 3 (February, 1953), p. 54.
25. Mayer, Albert, "What's the Matter with Our Site Plans?" *Pencil Points*, Vol. XXIII, No. 5 (May, 1942), p. 245.
26. Ministry of Housing and Local Government, Great Britain, *The Density of Residential Areas*. London, H.M.S.O., 1952.
27. Ministry of Town and Country Planning, Great Britain, "Site Planning and Layout in Relation to Housing," in *Design of Dwellings*. London, H.M.S.O., 1944.
28. Peets, Elbert, "Studies in Planning Texture." *Architectural Record*, Vol. 106, No. 3 (September, 1949), p. 131.
29. Robinson, Edwin, and Keeble, Lewis, *The Development of Building Estates*. London, Estates Gazette, 1952, Chaps. 14–21.
30. Royal Institute of British Architects, *Family Life in High Density Housing, with Particular Reference to the Design of Space about Buildings*. London, The Institute, 1957.
31. U. S. Federal Public Housing Authority, *Public Housing Design*. Washington, National Housing Agency, 1946.

Site Planning for Other Uses

32. American Society of Planning Officials, Planning Advisory Service, *Site Design, Parking and Zoning for Shopping Centers*, Information Report No. 59. Chicago, February, 1954.
33. Department of City and Regional Planning, M.I.T., *Institutional Expansion and the Urban Setting*. Cambridge, July, 1959.
34. Gruen, Victor, and Smith, Larry, *Shopping Towns USA*. New York, Reinhold, 1960.
35. Pasma, Theodore K., *Organized Industrial Districts*. Washington, U. S. Dept. of Commerce, Office of Technical Services, Area Development Division, 1954.

36. American Society of Civil Engineers, *Land Subdivision, Manual of Engineering Practice*, No. 16. New York, 1952.
37. Beranek, Leo L., ed., *Noise Reduction*. New York, McGraw-Hill, 1960.
38. Beazley, Elizabeth, *Design and Detail of the Space Between Buildings*. London, Architectural Press, 1960.
39. Dury, G. H., *The Face of the Earth*. London, Penguin, 1959.
40. Geiger, Rudolf, *The Climate Near the Ground*, trans. by Stewart. Cambridge, Harvard University Press, 1950.
41. Harris, Cyril M., ed., *Handbook of Noise Control*. New York, McGraw-Hill, 1957.
42. Matson, Theodore M., Smith, Wilbur S., and Hurd, Frederick W., *Traffic Engineering*. New York, McGraw-Hill, 1955.
43. National Committee for Traffic Safety, *Building Traffic Safety into Residential Developments*. Chicago, The Committee, 1950.
44. Manley, G., "Microclimatology." *Journal of the Royal Institute of British Architects*, Vol. 56, No. 7 (May, 1949), p. 317.
45. Parker, Harry, and MacGuire, John W., *Simplified Site Engineering for Architects and Builders*. New York, Wiley, 1954.
46. Rettinger, "Noise Level Reductions of Barriers." *Noise Control*, Vol. 3, No. 5 (September, 1952), p. 50.
47. Seelye, E. E., *Data Book for Engineers*, Vol. 1, *Design*. New York, Wiley, 1951.
48. Wyman, Donald, *Trees for American Gardens*. New York, Macmillan, 1951.

Pictorial References and Examples of Site Planning

49. Auzelle, Robert, *Documents d'Urbanisme*. Paris, Vincent Freal, 1947–1958.
50. Eden, William A., "Hampstead Garden Suburb: 1907–57." *Royal Institute of British Architects Journal*, Vol. 64 (October, 1957), p. 489.
51. Harada, Jiro, *Gardens of Japan*. London, Studio, 1928.
52. Hegemann, Werner, and Peets, Elbert, *The American Vitruvius*. New York, Architectural Book Publishing, 1922.
53. Rasmussen, Steen Eiler, *Towns and Buildings*. Cambridge, Harvard University Press, 1951.
54. Siren, Osvald, *Gardens of China*. New York, Ronald Press, 1949.
55. Smith, G. E. Kidder, *Italy Builds*. New York, Reinhold, 1955, pp. 40–117.
56. ——, *Sweden Builds*. New York, Reinhold, 1955, pp. 60–113.
57. Stein, Clarence S., *Towards New Towns for America*. Liverpool, University Press of Liverpool, 1951.
58. Wharton, Edith Newbold, *Italian Villas and Their Gardens*. New York, Century, 1904.
59. Wright, F. L., *Drawings for a Living Architecture*. New York, Horizon Press, 1959.
60. Zucker, Paul, *Town and Square: from the Agora to the Village Green*. New York, Columbia University Press, 1959.

List of Illustrations

Index*

* Italic page numbers refer to illustrations.